LEE COUNTY LIBRARY
107 Hawkins Ave.
Sanford, N. C. 27330

1795

T4-AEG-468

Sports After 50

(Fit Yourself Into Fun Sports)

By
Ted Overton

Medical Consultants: Robert P. Nirschl M.S., M.D.
Janet Sobel R.P.T.

Azimuth Press, Inc.
Annapolis, Maryland

Library of Congress Cataloguing in Publication Data

Overton, Ted
Sports After 50

1. Sports. 2. Physical education and training.
3. Middle age. 4. Sports for the aged. I. Title.
II. Title: Sports after fifty. III. Title: After 50.
IV. Title: After fifty.
GV706.8.094   1988   796'.01'926   88-70544
ISBN 0-913179-20-5

Copyright 1988 by Ted Overton

All rights reserved. No part of this book may be reproduced or transmitted in any form or by any means without the written permission of the publisher.

Azimuth Press, Inc.
15 N. Cherry Grove Ave.
Annapolis, MD 21401

Manufactured in the United States of America

Clarence C. Chaffee
August 26, 1901 — December 13, 1986

To "Chafe", whose joyous esprit, standards of sportsmanship and remarkable coaching career at Williams College showed so many of us that sports can be for life.

Acknowledgements

I doubt any author can truly recall every person who contributed to his or her project. And it is equally doubtful if, upon completion of the book, the author can accurately weigh the full extent of each contribution. A seemingly inconsequential suggestion generated in casual conversation, for example, may well become the spur for significant progress, whereas a thoughtful recommendation sometimes just doesn't fit.

So I thank each of my new acquaintances, old friends and family members who, on one or more occasions, willingly shared with me their thoughts about this book. You were caring about my project and generous with your time. I needed and am deeply appreciative of your help.

There is generally one individual, though, who ends up "keeping the fire lit". John Wooldridge, Executive Editor of Chesapeake Bay Magazine, starred in that thankless role. His belief in the book's message, his constant encouragement and his always astute criticism repeatedly nourished my efforts.

In turn, Wayne Carpenter, Publisher, Azimuth Press, took a deep breath and plunged enthusiastically into the task. Possibly, as a skilled ocean sailor turned avid boardsailor in his forties, he, too, is just getting ready for Sports After 50!

Foreword

It is often difficult for the layman to unravel the advertisements, recommendations and controversial claims which surround the subject of fitness and exercise.

More worrisome, relatively little attention has been paid to the concerns and misconceptions about fitness for that segment of Americans who are over 50 (more than 50,000,000 as of this date). Because so many of us reaching this age have, indeed, led overly sedentary lives, we should not jump into intensive conditioning programs. Yet, we need to start in the right direction.

SPORTS AFTER 50 ("Fit" Yourself Into Fun Sports) is an especially apt title since certain active sports provide direct conditioning benefits and also motivate one toward sound fitness habits. In this innovative and well illustrated book, Ted Overton has emphasized the kind of pertinent information about each sport that the beginner particularly needs, but that everyone should consider. He has also focused on the basic exercises needed to achieve base-line fitness on one hand, and to strengthen vulnerable areas of the body on the other.

This is a book for anyone interested in keeping active and mobile. It contains no magic formula but stresses what is practical and appropriate for the 50-and-over person to undertake. Most of us are subject to increasing "aches and pains" in our musculo-skeletal system as we age. Many of these symptoms, however, can be alleviated through the kind of sound preventive steps recommended here. Whether you read SPORTS AFTER 50 from beginning to end, or select certain chapters that seem of special interest, this book will provide important insights and extremely valuable advice.

Robert P. Nirschl, M.S., M.D.

Sports After 50

Table of Contents

Preface............1

Chapter I.........5.......**What's In It For You?**
　　　　　　　　　　　Medical evidence documents the role of exercise in improving the quality of life after 50.

Chapter II.......13.......**Which Sports?**
　　　　　　　　　　　Boardsailing................................. p. 22
　　　　　　　　　　　Biking.. p. 39
　　　　　　　　　　　Rowing...p. 51
　　　　　　　　　　　Racquet Sports............................ p. 65
　　　　　　　　　　　Canoeing..p. 85
　　　　　　　　　　　Skiing.. p. 97
　　　　　　　　　　　Swimming.................................... p. 115
　　　　　　　　　　　Small Boat Sailing.......................p. 122
　　　　　　　　　　　Hiking.. p. 131
　　　　　　　　　　　Outdoor Sports and Hypothermia..... p. 134

Chapter III.... 137.......**Getting Started**
　　　　　　　　　　　Simple and safe steps enable anyone to reach a base-line fitness level.

Chapter IV.... 159.......**Seniors' Competition**
　　　　　　　　　　　The new arena where camaraderie, fun and mutual sports interests are the key ingredients.

Chapter V..... 167.......**Women In Sports**
　　　　　　　　　　　Non-athletic women over 50 *can* regain their fitness and participate in sports.

Chapter VI.... 173.......**Nutritional Dangers: Supplements and Dieting**
　　　　　　　　　　　Pratical measures to separate the wheat from the chaff.

Chapter VII... 181.......Sports Medicine: The New Field Of Injury Prevention
Learning the special exercises that offer "preventive maintenance" protection for the vulnerable areas of the body.

Chapter VIII...211...... Go For It?
Avoiding all risk may be as harmful as taking a wrong one.

Illustration Credits.........215

Preface

No one can examine the role of exercise in enhancing the quality of life for those over fifty without recognizing the enormous contribution of Dr. Herbert A. deVries, Ph.D.* Prior to his studies and tests in the 1960's, the general medical consensus was that exercise did not benefit the health of the "elderly". Twenty-five years after he showed the way, his important concepts of improving muscle strength, endurance and flexibility have become universally accepted.

In health awareness as in most aspects of life, though, we seem to learn more from our mistakes or problems than from success. As I hit age 50, it took not one, but a whole series of back, arm, knee and ankle problems to point me toward realistic concepts of physical fitness.

*Herbert A. deVries, Ph.D., formerly Director of the Physiology Laboratory, Andrus Gerontology Center, University of Southern California, Los Angeles. Consultant, President's Council on Physical Fitness and Sports.

Even after exposure to the injury rehabilitation techniques of modern sports medicine, I failed to recognize that these remarkably effective methods are, essentially, short term unless one also is willing to practice the preventive medicine steps required by the musculo-skeletal part of our body. All I was interested in at the time was a cure. Surely, I thought, a special brace or, perhaps, some new pill could eliminate the pain and prevent further erosion of my mobility.

Eventually, Bob Nirschl (Dr. Robert P. Nirschl, M.S., M.D.*, founder, 1974, and Medical Director of the Virginia Sportsmedicine Institute), and Jan Sobel (Janet Sobel, R.P.T., Director of Rehabilitation), were able to educate me. In the process, they not only planted the seeds for this book, but became an integral part of its substance.

Their unique experience in developing and refining exercises to rehabilitate weak or damaged parts of the musculo-skeletal system, their constant emphasis on safe exercise patterns for the non athlete as well as for the athlete, and their responsiveness to all facets of fitness have made them the medical heart of this book.

The two questions we began to ponder several years ago were: Why don't more 50-and-over individuals participate in the fun and exercise benefits of appropriate sports? And which sports, in fact, are the right ones for an individual to begin at this age level?

My own background was a starting point of sorts. While mostly a recreational participant, I had enjoyed tennis and skiing over the years and had instructed informally in both. The pleasures of small boat sailing and canoeing also had been experienced. More recently, belated efforts to rehabilitate knee and ankle problems had acquainted me with the joys of the modern ten-speed bicycle. By chance, two quite different sports rolled across my horizon at this time.

---

*Robert P. Nirschl, M.S., M.D., Clinical Assistant Professor Georgetown University School of Medicine; Attending Orthopedic Surgeon, Arlington Hospital; Orthopedic Consultant, President's Council on Physical Fitness and Sports.

One of these was boardsailing (more popularly known as "windsurfing"). If my rehabilitating body could learn and enjoy this sport at age 60, then boardsailing might also fit many other seniors. Next, a friend (barred by emphysema from most active sports) urged me to try rowing in a modern shell. What a transformation from the old, flat-bottomed rowboat! So, rowing too, was a sport for all ages and one that offered the added advantage of being suitable for those with certain physical handicaps as well. In short, our research project was under way.

Over the next two years, all individual sports were examined and evaluated. Since exercise is so critical for fitness, the factor "exercise benefit" was initially very important in qualifying some sports for consideration — and in disqualifying others. It soon became apparent, however, that numerous other factors needed to be weighed, too. Eventually, eleven characteristics were defined. These could be applied to any sport and, collectively, would present an accurate profile of that sport's advantages and disadvantages in terms of an individual's interest, preferences and limitations.

It also became clear that the nationwide burst of interest in calisthenic exercises, and the resulting growth of health clubs, were not capturing many in the 50-and-over age category. Certainly, those of us who remember boot camp experience in 1941-1945 could testify to the effectiveness of calisthenics (though most of those drill sergeants hadn't looked in such great shape!). But at our present age, who wants a drill sergeant to monitor fitness? In fact, evidence continued to indicate that fitness, as an isolated standard, has little appeal to the 50-and-over person who has settled into a rather sedentary life style. Conversely, whenever good fitness habits have become part of someone's life, this interest almost always relates to some sport activity they enjoy.

So, more and more the answer seemed to lay in introducing individuals to the right sports; fun sports that would motivate, active sports that would help condition the body. The challenge would be to eliminate the numerous misconceptions and fears that have so negatively affected the attitudes of the majority of 50-and-older persons towards sports participation. At the same time, pertinent questions about the safety of physical exercise, conflicting nutritional information, and other aspects of fitness and health at this age needed to be examined.

The result is this book with its two interweaving themes: The selection and characterization of the most suitable sports, and a program enabling one to easily reach and maintain the base-line fitness for safely learning and enjoying these sports.

If a sport isn't fun, don't do it. We think you will find at least one — and, hopefully, several among the nine sports described — which will add greatly to your enjoyment of life as well as to your fitness.

Ted Overton
Fairfax, Virginia
April, 1988

Chapter I
What's In It For You?

Most of us reaching 50 have not only neglected our physical condition in terms of overall fitness, but also tend to have poor fitness habits. Although numerous books, magazines and video tapes are ready to introduce us to physical fitness programs (including some that focus specifically on those 50 and older), there still has been no rush to fitness by members of our age group.

Nor is there likely to be, as long as fitness programs emphasize primarily a regimen of rigorous calisthenic-type exercises. Our long-time habits of little or no exercise (even excluding those extra sins of junk food, extensive smoking, too much alcohol and other over-indulgences) are not easily altered. Without some special motivation, few are willing to accept the discipline and boredom of typical exercise programs.

Some of us also have tried the shortcuts to fitness. Those fad diets for weight control and the "five-minute workouts" for muscle strengthening are just snares. They not only don't work, they often are counter productive. At the other extreme, an intensive program of calisthenics is hardly enticing. Of more concern, a too rigorous program featuring an over-zealous dive into a "New You" actually can be dangerous. The concept is unwise at any age, but the body responds especially poorly to sudden and grand scale changes as we become older. At best, this type of quick fix is impossible to achieve and can generate long-term harm as well as short-term pain.

Fortunately, there is a happy alternative that combines exercise with fun and is open to most of us — participation in those active sports that someone 50-and-over can begin safely and enjoy throughout life. These sports lead to fitness habits that invigorate instead of frustrate, stimulate rather than tire, condition not weary.

To select one or more of these sports, you should know how well a particular sport will fit your interests, general physique and limitations. To assist you, we have examined each sport's pertinent characteristics from the perspective of a beginner. Such factors as the ease and difficulty of learning, local and regional availability, equipment and other costs, fitness level required, aerobic benefits, time considerations, and special skills needed are among the distinctive characteristics evaluated. The result: a realistic profile of each sport emerges, one that clearly portrays whether that sport can fit you (Chapter II).

Perhaps, though, you have heard that sports exercise can be dangerous for the older person. It can, if it is the wrong sport and if one neglects basic conditioning. Participating in active sports that fit your physique, health and existing physical condition involves exercise that contributes to productive fitness. Achieving that kind of fitness is what this book is all about.

So what is productive fitness? Is it a level of fitness we can and need to reach? A lot of potentially active and wonderful years are out there beyond 50. Is exercise really such an important component of fitness?

Make no mistake; the evidence is now in and the answers are clear. Fitness indeed has a dramatic impact on the quality of life one can expect from 50 on, and the key to fitness at any age — not just for the young — is appropriate physical exercise. If you remain a doubter, consider the following facts: There is a well defined physical decline as one ages. Commencing at age 30, the average person loses functional capacity (muscular and overall physical motion capability) at the rate of between 0.75% and 1% each year. So, at age 60, the loss is somewhere between 23% and 30%; almost 40% by age 70 and 50% by 80. Yet, medical research has determined that up to half that loss is preventable. The essential ingredient in achieving such a significant improvement? Proper physical exercise.

Why are the researchers so sure? In addition to numerous and convincing tests given to various age groups as well as to individuals of differing fitness levels (and which measured the degree to which proper exercise improved their fitness), perhaps the most persuasive evidence emerged from measuring the decline in fitness level when exercise was eliminated. A group of well-conditioned young men underwent enforced total bed rest for a period of three weeks. Virtually no exercise of any kind was allowed. When their functional capacity was measured at the end of the period, the loss for each was the equivalent of 30 years of aging! No illness, no diet problems, no new stress — just no exercise.

Not convincing enough? Well, look at it from a different angle. Did you ever consider how many times your heart beats each day? In the 50 to 60 age group, for example, pulse rate at rest will be between 70 and 75 for the average healthy person. Even at the lower range, that means approximately 100,000 beats per day or roughly 36,500,000 beats per year.

It has been proven that a sound fitness program can reduce a person's heart rate by about 10 beats per minute (and the decrease often is greater). Then the figures would decline to around 86,000 beats per day, or 31,500,000 beats per year. This is a "saving" of 5,000,000 beats annually! Go on, do the arithmetic yourself covering the next 10, 20, 30 or more years you should be enjoying. This is not to say that a slower heart rate is automatically healthier than a faster one. But, are you really willing to ignore such possible assistance for that wonderful engine, your heart?

Finally, there is the impressive continuing study of nearly 17,000 Harvard alumni, and described in the March, 1986 issue of New England Journal of Medicine. These individuals had entered the university between 1916 and 1950 and completed extensive questionnaires in 1962 and 1966 about their health status and exercise habits. Their records were followed through 1978. Among the older alumni, the risk of death for those physically active was half that of the least active. Dr. Ralph S. Paffenbarger, Jr., M.D., of the Stanford University School of Medicine, and director of the study, puts it succinctly: "There are lots of skeptics who say people are active because they are healthy. These findings support the view that you're healthy because you are active." The report concludes that "...inheritance of a sturdy constitution is less important to longevity than continuation of adequate lifetime exercise."

Unfortunately, the word fitness is both overused and abused today. At the very least, a wrong concept is being exploited through such images as bulging muscles, the "body beautiful" or other extremes. Of even more concern are the many new products being promoted in all media to capitalize on the burgeoning health and fitness market.

Commencing with a seemingly limitless number of over-the-counter vitamins and other "health-promoting products" and extending to a wide variety of home fitness equipment, so-called fitness products are deluging the public. Assuming one is not under a doctor's care, there are two important considerations here for everyone:

1. There is no special diet to assure fitness. Good nutrition, on the other hand, is vitally important. There also is no evidence that mega-vitamins or special foods will foster health or vitality. On the contrary, some of these may actually damage your health (Chapter VI).

2. You don't need a home gym or health club facilities to achieve productive fitness for your age level. Some equipment can be helpful in bad weather. Indiscriminate use of exercise machines, though, can injure, not strengthen the body (Chapter VII).

There also is a vast difference between being just "out of shape" and in having a basic weakness or malfunction in your cardiovascular or musculo-skeletal systems. While problems within the musculo-skeletal system generally are self evident (back or other joint pain is never hidden!), cardiovascular flaws can be deceptively masked. No one can afford not to have a thorough examination of their cardiovascular system performed by a physician familiar with their own and their family's health history.

As discussed in Chapter III, Getting Started, a base-line health evaluation is critical. Although a healthy cardiovascular system is essential for developing stamina, there is some disagreement within the medical profession as to the desirable level of stamina and best methods for achieving this level, in particular, the importance of aerobic exercise. Nevertheless, the arguments in support of aerobic exercise are persuasive. Because aerobic exercise places some extra demands on the cardiovascular system, many doctors recommend that anyone 50 or over (some doctors say 40 and over) should also include a physical stress test (a further tool in evaluating cardiovascular health) as part of the basic physical examination prior to commencing a fitness program.

Whether or not one engages in aerobic exercise, it is important to recognize that there is no total immunity to the possibility of incurring cardiovascular disease (even though a low cholesterol diet appears to be sound preventive medicine). Those with a family history of heart disease must be especially watchful. Symptoms of cardiovascular malfunctions, however, should never be ignored by anyone no matter their apparent fitness. Failure to recognize or accept this fact has occasionally led to headline "keel-overs" by some well-known athletes. These are not only tragic personal and family losses, but also generate negative publicity about that particular sport and even about exercise in general. What does not make the headlines, though, (and thus is mostly overlooked) is subsequent medical analysis concerning the cause of the collapse. This almost always has disclosed that it was not the particular sport that initiated the failure, but rather the existence of a flaw in that person's cardiovascular system which the individual knew about , but chose to ignore.

The realities of cardiovascular weakness, however, are not necessarily disastrous. Interestingly, appropriate exercise, under the supervision of a cardiovascular specialist, often can improve the fitness and overall health of someone with such a malfunction.

Most of us are lucky enough to have a healthy cardiovascular system that can be further supported by good fitness habits. It is the stiffness, aches and discomfort in our musculo-skeletal system that tend to deter us from regular exercise and the enjoyment of active sports. Today, sports medicine techniques have revolutionized the treatment and cure of many musculo-skeletal problems. Evolving from the requirements of professional sports, this new profession has developed therapy techniques that often result in a stronger function than before the injury. Equally, if not more important, sports medicine emphasizes the kind of preventive measures that actually reduce the chance of injury (Chapter VII).

But if fear of injury still holds you back from sports participation, consider the following points. First, the majority of musculo-skeletal problems (back, shoulder and other joint discomfort) and direct injuries occur not from sports participation but from some every-day routine such as tripping on steps or curbs, lifting too much weight or lifting incorrectly. Second, it is generally the person who is not fit who suffers such injuries and who receives the more serious ones. Finally, it is the inactive and less fit individual who, when injured, has greater difficulty in making a full recovery.

As you examine each of the sports covered in Chapter II, you will note that two of the characteristics evaluated, *fitness required* and *injury potential* also pinpoint those areas of the body that may need strengthening as you further engage in that particular sport. That is important advice and you should refer to the appropriate exercises as noted in Chapter VII. This type of preventive medicine not only will be facilitating your proficiency and pleasure in that sport, but also will be improving overall body strength.

No two of us are built exactly the same and differing torso shapes affect the kind of leverage we can and should apply to our body. Learning to know your own body, its weaker as well as its stronger points, is important. Developing this understanding and using one's body intelligently is a key part of productive fitness.

Good fitness, however, is not all you gain from active sports. Today, a wide variety of fun sports' competition is available for seniors. You may be surprised to learn that participants of every skill level are encouraged to compete within their age categories. In effect, seniors' competition is not for the professional, expert or elite athlete. Instead, it is oriented around those who enjoy the sport and the camaraderie of informal competition (Chapter IV).

While all the sports reviewed are as suitable for 50 and older women as for men, women in this age category often need extra encouragement due to two factors. First, most received little sports background during their school years. Second, most have had fewer opportunities than men, overall, to develop coordinated muscular strengths.

As Chapter V emphasizes, however, these handicaps need not be permanent. Not only can good musculo-skeletal functions be regained, but the base-line fitness needed for safe and enjoyable participation in sports can be achieved in a relatively brief period. Even if a disease like osteoporosis has weakened bone structure, appropriate exercise often can assist vital rehabilitation efforts. And, medical advice now stresses that exercise plus good nutrition can effectively defend against osteoporosis in later years.

As a final chapter, some views are expressed about risk taking. If there is a natural tendency to become more cautious as one ages (generated in part by the wisdom of experience), there also is a less fortuitous corollary, namely, the tendency to eliminate all risk. Yet, exploring new horizons seems to be an important part of health at any age, particularly for seniors. Inevitably, there can be some risk in the process, but the greater loss is to withdraw from such efforts and to lose incentive. The fitness, enjoyment and stimulus you will experience through sports will nourish this valuable energy source. Begin today. You'll enjoy more of tomorrow.

Chapter II

Which Sports For You?

If you have never played any sport — or perhaps were once active, then stopped some years ago and now are convinced it's too late to update old and learn new skills — or, you suddenly felt a twinge in your aching "sympathetic" joint after reading the title of this chapter, don't back away now. The sports discussed here can be learned and enjoyed by the reasonably fit person at almost any age! And, of course, whatever sports you enjoy now, keep them up. Hopefully, this chapter will introduce some new sports that will both attract you and fit your needs.

First, however, remember that basic fitness comes before active sports involvement, so you should choose either walking, bicycling or swimming as an initial conditioning program and build up slowly to the exercise level recommended in Chapter III, Getting Started. Once you are comfortable with this base-line fitness, you are ready for sports. But now, put aside any existing pre-conceptions about sports in general, or about a particular sport, and consider these two points:

- The sports recommended here are sports you can play for life.
- At least one — and probably several — of these sports will fit your general physique, background interest, available free time and other criteria of importance to you.

You don't need to be tremendously knowledgeable about a sport in order to learn and enjoy it. Just understand that each sport offers features that will be a plus or a minus depending upon your needs and interests, not on someone else's criteria. The aim is not to find the single sport that seems "correct" for you, but to recognize all those sports which qualify for your likely enjoyment. The sports you select should work for you , not vice-versa!

There are numerous misconceptions — if not myths — about many sports. Such phrases as: "Too difficult to learn, too strenuous, too dangerous, too seasonal," etc., often are accepted as gospel, even though recent advances in equipment, technique and protective clothing have greatly reduced the validity of such comments. The fact that you have never participated in a particular sport doesn't mean you can't learn it quite quickly or won't enjoy it. Just make sure you, not some self-styled expert, make this evaluation.

To assist you, we've listed the main characteristics that, to a greater or lesser degree, apply to every sport. There is no attempt to rank these in importance. Certain characteristics will be more important to some readers, while different ones will influence others.

Collectively, these characteristics portray the full dimensions of a sport. Depending upon the weighting you give to each of these factors, a sort of individualized profile of the sport emerges, a profile that should indicate quite clearly the suitability of that sport for you. Take a moment to review this list before turning to the section summarizing each sport. Give extra thought to the factors Fitness Level for Playing and Injury Potential. In addition to providing a realistic fitness yardstick for each sport, those appraisals evaluate the potential range of exertion, the kinds of extra physical stress that can be experienced and the chances of injury.

In some instances, we have suggested specific conditioning exercises to strengthen particular parts of the body. The point is not to alarm, but to alert you to the fact that selected exercises will both reduce chances of unnecessary injury and also develop the physical capacity to fully enjoy the sport.

Sport Characteristics

EASE OF LEARNING

In essence, this evaluation judges the complexity of (a) the concepts involved in the sport, (b) the specific techniques that must be learned and (c) the physical movements required in execution. It is a combination of these elements that determine whether a sport is easier or more difficult to learn.

WEATHER AND/OR SEASONAL LIMITS

Some sports traditionally have labored under specific climate limitations or have projected a distinctly "one season" image. While the weather factor and desirable temperature range always are worth knowing, modern sports equipment and specialized materials for sport clothes (inner as well as outer garments) have added new seasonal versatility to many sports.

TIME EXPENDED

The amount of time needed to play the sport can also determine whether it suits your own life style. Just learning the sport is one kind of investment in time. Some sports require time consuming preparations and take a relatively long time to play, while others require little time.

INITIAL AND RECURRING COSTS

Considered here is the initial expense of equipment plus other support costs (factors such as whether public or private facilities are generally used, rental fees for specialized equipment, etc.). In addition, there can be costs for instruction, frequent "wear-out" items, plus replacement of major equipment.

LOCAL AND/OR REGIONAL AVAILABILITY

Are the facilities for local use generally easy to reach and accessible at times best for you? Is it a purely local sport, or can you also engage in it away from home? In short, is it really available and can you take this sport with you when you travel?

FITNESS LEVEL FOR PLAYING

We are not going to grade sports for this category, but you should know what to expect in terms of the physical exertion and fitness necessary to enjoy the sport. "Enjoying a sport" really means playing it at an intensity level that challenges you, encourages learning further skills, and rewards you through a feeling of accomplishment.

SKILL LEVEL FOR ENJOYMENT

This factor is related to "Fitness Level", but there is a distinct difference. Some sports require a relatively high level of playing skill for real satisfaction (and, in fact, to avoid feeling actual frustration.). Others have lower outright skill requirements. For example, "hand/eye" coordination is important in racquet sports, while factors such as a sense of rythm or good balance are more important for other sports.

AEROBIC QUALITIES

Again, this is not a plus or minus feature, but at least you should be realistic about the degree of aerobics a sport can provide. Significant aerobics value can enhance a sport's desirability for many and, in any case, it is hard to imagine this as a negative factor (unless, of course, a person is under a doctor's restrictive recommendations).

INJURY POTENTIAL

Everyone should consider this factor in a sport. Just don't let it frighten you; sitting in a chair isn't injury-proof either! The basic

Which Sports For You?

point: in this sport, is there a likelihood of incurring an injury and, if one occurs, is it apt to cause minor, moderate or extensive damage? The assumption is that you will use good judgment while involved and thus simply need to be aware of the injury risk level inherent in that sport. Vulnerability from old injuries, of course, always is an added risk.

CAN YOU ENJOY IT ALONE?

This point hardly needs to be defined and certainly, only you can determine its importance. If your schedule defies advance planning, then you and your playing partners will be frustrated over your schedule changes while, if your sport doesn't require another person, you are more flexible. Some sports obviously are primarily "alone". Some can be enjoyed either alone or with others. Some require an opponent or at least another person for the sport to be played.

SOCIABILITY

This is quite separate from the previous point. We're not concerned here with the number of individuals necessary or involved in playing the sport, but with the general sociability generated by the sport. Is there more or less of a friendly atmosphere connected with the sport. For example, does there seem to be an easy camaraderie among the participants? Does the sport appear to attract individuals of one's general age group? Watch the sport in action a few times and you'll soon discover the degree of sociability it stimulates.

As you examine these sports, you may be surprised at some of those included, as well as the ones that are not. But before all those enthusiastic golfers, fishermen, bowlers and hunters take umbrage over their sport's exclusion, we hope they will reflect on our selection criteria:

- This is not a listing of good as opposed to bad sports.
- This is a review of those enjoyable sport activities which can best contribute to the general conditioning and fitness of those in the 50 and older category.

All of the above four sports are certainly highly enjoyable and healthy activities. They do not, however, fit the rest of the criteria. The millions who play them should not be offended. We are not saying, "Don't play those sports." We are saying, "If you don't play any sport now and are intent upon improving your fitness level, then here are the sports activities you should consider."

In fact, if some of you inveterate bowlers, golfers, hunters and fishermen would care to try another sport, we think you, too, may find this section a useful menu. Team sports enthusiasts also may feel we have dealt with them unfairly. For example, what about that wonderful group of 70 to 90 year-olds who continue to play softball? How terrific! They should never stop! But these and their lesser aged contemporaries who continue such team sports as soccer, ice hockey, basketball, touch football and others, are truly a special category. The key word here is "continue". These participants are continuing to play a sport they still love and played extensively when younger. Whatever the risk of injury, they feel this is more than balanced by the unique camaraderie of team play, exhilaration and competitive stimulation they reap. The rest of us may well envy them, but we must look to other sports for those benefits.

And then there are those individual sports that can't easily be categorized, can certainly be pursued through advancing age, yet also are omitted from our list. Why not consider sports like horseback riding, fencing, ice skating, kayaking and even hang gliding? We were tempted, because in some ways they qualify and those individuals who still participate in them generally are physically fit. These sports were excluded because the potential injury level is too high for someone *commencing* them at age 50-and-over. To repeat, it is one thing to continue playing such sports as age advances; to start them when older is quite another. We are not saying it can't be done, only that we cannot recommend it.

Finally, there are the runners — both joggers and marathoners. How can the sport which is properly credited with turning millions of Americans toward better fitness not be considered here? Unfortunately, as excellent as running can be for aerobic conditioning of younger men and women, the pounding that ankles, knees, hips and the lower back receive can become a problem for those over 50 and be particularly troublesome for those in that age category who have not recently been regular runners.

Yes, running — and track events in general — is a well established sport in Senior Olympics. Even most of the road races currently being scheduled include senior age classifications from 35 to 65 and older. So, if you already run and are free from joint problems, there is, indeed, interesting competition for peer-age groups. If you are not now a runner and/or are just commencing a fitness program, we urge that you first condition yourself with brisk walking. Then try a speed walking program. If there are no symptoms of ankle, knee or back sensitivity, perhaps you are one of those fortunate few seniors whose physique can withstand the more constant pounding of jogging and running. You alone can be the judge.

There are, of course, other sports that could be mentioned but were excluded for one or more of the above reasons. And so, at last, it came down to the nine sports activities recommended here. We are confident that each of them (that meet your personal criteria) can contribute safely to your fitness, while adding a lively and enjoyable dimension to your life.

INSTRUCTION — A SMART INVESTMENT

A frequent statement by those who don't participate in sports is: "I tried it but couldn't do it."

On close examination, this generally means that they tried to learn without proper instruction. Nine times out of ten, the results of this approach are discouraging. What can be worse, the extreme frustration generated during the unsuccessful learning attempt can also include improper muscle use, leading to strain or other injury. At the very least, the individual is "turned off" from that sport. Similar discouragement in another sport inevitably results in that person concluding, "Sports are not for me. I'm not athletic enough." That's a double loss!

As with other fields, there is no substitute for good instruction in learning a sport. For the most part, it should be a qualified professional. At minimum, it should be someone who knows the sport thoroughly, has had successful experience teaching it and is enthused about helping you learn the sport correctly.

There are several advantages in learning through a professional. First, you can question others who have gone through that course (their enthusiasm, lack of it, or other comments can tell you a lot about the quality of instruction). Second, the professional course should provide a helpful summary of the instruction, plus having on hand other useful information about the sport. The "good friend" who is skilled in the sport also can be satisfactory. Just make sure such a person has the right equipment, good instructional aids, a proper location for instruction and knows how to teach a beginner.

Some sports require more initial instruction than others, but with proper instruction, you should experience beginning success and fun the first day in learning any of the sports recommended here. How much instruction you should have depends a lot on you. Some sports offer a beginning course. If you complete that, you are ready to proceed on your own, which means you now can (and should) practice independently what you have learned. In the process, you will start to gain confidence, improve your technique and may even try more advanced steps that will prepare you to move on to the next level. This is not, however, a license to think, "Well, I can handle this sport!"

Most sports generally recognize four performance levels: beginner, intermediate, advanced and expert. The majority of us settle for intermediate. It's a level at which we feel confident, the exercise is good, and the sport is fun and companionable. A number, however, enjoy mastering the more complicated steps which lead to advanced. Few, if any, who take up a sport at our age will reach the expert level. Oh yes, on good days there is a tendency to think, "Wow! I'm hot!" Just don't get carried away and believe it.

Proceeding from beginner to intermediate may or may not require further instruction. It depends upon the sport and also upon one's athletic ability, level of fitness and the way one learns. Yes, there's a difference in this last point. Some of us learn best through oral instruction, others respond better to visual demonstration. If you are in the latter category, you often can improve technique just by watching and imitating those who are more skilled than you. Watch an alpine skiing class of 6 and 8 year-olds. There's almost no oral instruction. They just follow the instructor's movements. Unfortunately, at our age it's not so easy to learn the same way.

One process for determining if someone is a competent instructor (and perhaps more importantly, would be effective in teaching you) is to watch an instructional class. Some points to look for:

- Is the instructor communicative in a clear way?
- Does the instructor prefer talking about what interests him or her rather than taking time for demonstrating and explaining key learning steps?
- Is sufficient time allowed for questions?
- Are slow students encouraged or made to feel unsuccessful by comparison with others?
- Is it evident the instructor thoroughly knows the sport?
- Is the instructor enthusiastic about teaching the class or is it obvious this is, "Just a job," for him or her?
- Does the instructor seem to get the best out of each student?

In sum, anyone taking up a sport should invest in good instruction. The expense of getting started correctly through instruction is really minimal. Good instruction is not a luxury. Rather, it is the best possible investment toward your full enjoyment of any sport.

BOARDSAILING

If you are surprised to find boardsailing also is a sport for those 50-and-over, you are not alone. Most newcomers to this sport are amazed to discover it offers so many levels of enjoyment, is quite easy to learn, can provide moderate or strenuous exercise, and there is a minimum of risk of injury. You will see boardsailors aged 8 to 80, so it is truly a family sport.

Remember to smile

"But," you may be thinking, "what about those video shots of boardsailors upside down and ten feet over the waves? You are crazy to suggest that for my aging body!"

Well, both of us are right and this paradox is precisely why boardsailing is a sport for all ages and ability levels. Yes, your children and grandchildren could possibly become sufficiently expert to jump waves like the TV films show. You, too, could also reach the same skill level, but the risk in wave jumping is obviously fairly high. You really wouldn't try ski jumping now, would you, even though alpine and cross country skiing are considered suitable sports for all ages?

The boardsailing you will do, on the contrary, is strictly on the water, though occasionally, mostly while learning, you also might

Which Sports For You?

be in the water. The basic physical requirements: a reasonable sense of balance and a strength level equivalent to that of the average 12-year-old boy or girl.

As with all sports associated with water, one should be a competent swimmer. You will not do much actual swimming, but you should feel confident and comfortable when a fall puts you in the water. The sailboard won't drift away and it is easy to climb back on. Life jackets can be worn while boardsailing and are mandatory in some regions. The bulky Kapok-type life preserver is too cumbersome for practicality, but the modern, flatter preserver can be worn comfortably. Some of the special safety factors offered by boardsailing are: (1) a sailboard is truly unsinkable; (2) if the wind dies or the rigging breaks, the sail can be rolled up and placed on the sailboard or discarded if weather conditions are too extreme. The sailor then paddles back to shore by kneeling or lying flat on the board; (3) one can rest while paddling, and if there is a contrary tide or current, the board can still be paddled successfully, whereas a swimmer could not make headway.

So, you will be taking up a sport that is extremely safe, exhilarating and can provide exercise that ranges from modest to energetic. It has a number of other characteristics that also may surprise you.

EASE OF LEARNING

Don't try to learn on your own! You simply will become fatigued and frustrated without learning the techniques. Good instructional facilities will be located near sailing areas and generally will offer both a three-hour and six-hour course. The former will get you sailing in an afternoon, but the latter is a very worthwhile investment, particularly if you have had little experience in a regular sailboat.

The six-hour course first teaches you the sailing, positioning and steering techniques on a land simulator. The confidence gained here makes the move to the water easy and you will be sailing immediately.

With either course, though, the learning process is fast. A small sail makes it easy to pull up the mast and balancing is far simpler than it looks. Much of the time you are just leaning back against the pull of the sail. Progress comes rapidly and every time you boardsail, you learn more. Fun while learning really applies to this sport.

SPORTS AFTER 50

A land simulator teaches you how to climb onto the sailboard...

...To use your leg muscles (note the bent knees) when pulling up the mast/sail rig...

... And to find the correct mast position for keeping the sailboard on a steady course.

Which Sports For You?

The same techniques are used on the water after a fall. First, you climb back on the sailboard ...

Next, pull up the mast/sail rig ...

Then adjust the mast forward or backward to the best position for your new course.

25

SEASONAL LIMITATIONS

Modern wetsuits and dry suits make this sport enjoyable through six to nine months along the north Atlantic coast and in the Midwest. The sport can be year around in Florida, the Caribbean islands and

Hat, jacket and a "Long John" wetsuit provide comfortable sailing on an October day in New England.

most of the West Coast. Wetsuits are comfortable to wear, attractive looking and are designed for a variety of weather conditions. Suits come in one or two pieces, "shorties", and in different thicknesses. Also available are gloves, booties and head gear. Basically, the wetsuit maintains body warmth, which otherwise escapes due to the wind chill factor. Even in summer, it is good to have at least a wetsuit top available for those cool, windy days when the sailing is great but the spray, if not a spill, can chill you!

TIME EXPENDED

A sailboard can be stored in a garage (or even outside), is easily carried on a car rack, and, at the water, can be rigged in five or ten minutes. Thus, someone with limited free time can spend most of it actually sailing, not just getting ready.

Which Sports For You?

Once on the water, an hour of boardsailing can both be enjoyable relaxation and good exercise. The only wasted time is traveling to where one plans to sail. Fortunately, a large body of water is not needed for boardsailing. One can have great fun on a small lake. Lacking a tide or current, lake sailing is nice for beginners.

INITIAL AND RECURRING COSTS

A good, used sailboard and rig will stand up well and give you many hours of sailing pleasure while you advance your skills. After you have sailed a while, you will be better qualified to know which kind of sailboard best fits your needs. There are a number of manufacturers and models.

Generally, the instructional school where you learn will have both new and used boards for sale. If there is a local sailing fleet near you, it is best to get the type of board sailed in that fleet so you can join in regattas and participate on an even basis.

The newer model sailboards are somewhat more fragile than older ones, but also are lighter, faster and even more fun to sail. Most boards can be repaired easily and, with moderate care, will provide years of good sailing. This applies to the mast and boom, too. If you start racing, you will want to buy an additional sail ($245-$300 plus) to keep just for those events.

So far, the wind and the water are free, although some state parks and marinas charge a small launching fee.

REGIONAL AVAILABILITY

Basic Instruction:
3 hour course: $40
6 hour course: $60-$75
Purchase of sailboard and rig:
New: $550-$1500 plus
Used $250-$400
Rentals: $35-$50 per day

Since one can boardsail on small lakes, rivers, bays and harbors,

SPORTS AFTER 50

Bob Wright, 73, of North Palm Beach, FL, easily carries the mast/sail rig.

He slides the universal joint at the bottom of the mast into a special fitting on the sailboard.

Which Sports For You?

... And pulls the board and rig into the water.

Then he lifts up the mast and steps aboard for an easy beach start.

SPORTS AFTER 50

Bringing your sailboard with you is no problem. First, put the front of the board on top of the rear section of the car rack, then slide the board forward until it balances on the rack. Tie down securely. Most racks allow two sailboards to fit nicely, even on a small car.

Which Sports For You?

in addition to the ocean, most sections of the U.S. provide good sailing choices within easy reach by car (and sailboards are light enough to be car-topped by a woman alone).

If you are traveling far, a few airlines will allow you to ship your board and rig with other luggage. The possibility of damage, especially to the mast, makes this less attractive. The best advice, if traveling by air to a resort is to rent your board. Most resort facilities offer both instruction and rental boards. They also will know the local sailing conditions, which is something you should always check out first before sailing in unknown waters.

FITNESS LEVEL REQUIRED

The fact that boardsailing can fit such a wide age range is a wonderful feature. On one hand, this means that individuals with limited physical strength such as children, adults with a slight build and older persons, can fully enjoy the sport. This is achieved by using a much smaller sail, not only when learning but also when the wind is strong. Actually, in high winds, the board responds better to a smaller sail (unless one is quite skilled), the physical exertion is reduced, yet there is relatively little loss of speed.

On the other hand, as one's proficiency increases, so does the desire to sail as fast as one can, execute the exciting maneuvers possible on a sailboard, and to race in regattas. A unique pleasure of this sport is the speed the board achieves as it starts to plane across the water when the winds reach about 12 miles per hour. The sensation of "flying" grows as the wind speed increases.

The technique of sailing in higher winds is not difficult to learn, but there also are increased physical demands, primarily on the arms, shoulders and stomach muscles. Correct boardsailing posture is important and is another good argument in favor of getting professional instruction when beginning. Even in moderate winds, if you use your back to "hang on", you open yourself to back strain. Correct posture, on the other hand, will help strengthen the stomach muscles, while shoulders, arms, wrists and fingers are getting a workout, too. Sailing in ocean waves, or in any rough water, is both added fun and good exercise for ankles, knees and legs.

In sum, the range of enjoyment in this sport allows different levels of fitness and strength. Since most individuals who learn boardsailing soon want to sail in stronger winds, an exercise program that strengthens stomach muscles, as well as shoulders and arms, is highly recommended.

SKILL LEVEL FOR ENJOYMENT

There is a certain tediousness in learning any sport, but boardsailing has less than most because the basic skills can be learned so quickly. Having learned to steer and control the board, there is immediate pleasure in just sailing. At the same time, the sporting enjoyment of sailing fast, maneuvering the board more radically, and handling rough water, all require some additional skills and more precise movements.

A good sense of balance becomes increasingly important in higher winds. Advanced boardsailing, though, is more a sense of feeling the wind and reacting automatically to the changing pressures on the sail. If, on one hand, it is true that you have to hold up the mast and sail, it is equally true that the wind pressure on the sail holds you up. In other words, the boardsailor seemingly leaning out precariously over the water is really just equalizing the pull of the sail in the other direction. Balance in boardsailing is not a tight-rope act, but rather the use of your body's weight to counter an opposing force.

In fact, the skill level required to sail in strong winds, to race competitively and to maneuver quickly doesn't require new and different techniques as much as it needs refinement and precision in performing the basic techniques one originally learns. Everyone takes some spills while adjusting and practicing these techniques, so remember to bring along your humility as you reach out to experience the many dimensions of this sport.

AEROBIC QUALITIES

When the wind is "up", boardsailing will provide efficient aerobic training. Below a wind strength of 10 miles per hour, however, there is little aerobic demand, although a number of body muscles still will receive good exercise.

Which Sports For You?

Changing direction radically while sailing down wind is a fun maneuver. Harry Biffar, 69, of Boynton Beach, FL, has commenced turning and has just allowed the sail (still on the left side of the board) to start swinging forward by releasing his back (left) hand from the boom.

The sail has completed its swing around the mast as the board keeps turning to the left. It now is on the right side of the sailboard and Harry again has both hands on the boom.

Completing the turn, he heads back across the wind, in a direction approximately 90 degrees to the left of his course when starting the turn (top photo).

SPORTS AFTER 50

Note how he leans back and keeps his center of gravity low as the wind increases, thus balancing the pull of the sail in the opposite direction.

An inner harbor is ideal for learning. Beginning skills can be practiced safely while the open water beyond can provide the varied conditions needed to advance one's skills.

Which Sports For You?

INJURY POTENTIAL

Normal boardsailing poses few injury hazards. Since you are standing practically at the water level, falling in the rest of the way is unlikely to be injurious. Even at higher speeds, the fall is still only a big splash and bruises only the ego.

It also is possible to fall over on top of the boom or mast after these have already fallen into the water. At most, you may get a slight bruise from that contact. If you fall over backward and pull the mast and sail over too, then an upraised hand will ward off possible contact with the mast.

Beginning boardsailors, however, should only sail in protected waters and preferably when there is an on-shore (wind blowing toward the shore) wind. Until you are sufficiently skilled to tack upwind, a strong off-shore breeze could prevent you from getting back to land. In addition, beginning boardsailors should not sail in areas with constant powerboat traffic. Despite the traditional rule giving sail right-of-way over power, you are vulnerable on a sailboard unless you can maneuver quickly and surely.

SOCIABILITY

Although boardsailing needs no partner (one is both captain and crew on this sailboat!), the informality of this sport is contagious. It is a great family activity, and boardsailing regattas are fun social events as well as friendly competition. Women sail equally with the male species and their lighter weight often gives them an advantage. Most regattas give women the choice of sailing in a separate class or in a combined men/women class. In addition, a growing number of regattas now include a seniors' or Masters' category in which age groups of 45-54; 55-64; and 65 and over compete with their peers.

A few years ago, people wondered at that strange looking board and sail perched on top of the car they just passed. Today, this is a frequent sight and is likely to get you a friendly wave of a hand when your car also carries one!

SPORTS AFTER 50

Doris Briar, 64, or Latana Beach, FL, makes a good beach start. She wears a wetsuit to counter the cool breezes of early spring.

Moving out into deeper water, she pushes the daggerboard down with her back (right) foot so the sailboard won't slip sideways

Speed picks up as she adjusts the mast and boom to keep the sail full and steers the sailboard across the wind.

Which Sports For You?

The 45-54 age division gets off to a fast start at the 1987 National Senior Sailboard Championships held September 10-13 at Hilton Head Island, SC.

BICYCLING

Do you remember your first bike and the new world that biking opened up? Why did we ever stop? Oh yes, we grew up, didn't we? That was it — off to college and/or a job, and a car soon became a must.

Perhaps you tried biking again when your children reached that same exciting age ("Gee, Mom, I didn't know you could ride!"). Well, even if that period didn't arouse your old enthusiasm, haven't you felt just a little envious occasionally as one of those modern 10-speed marvels zipped by?

So what's keeping you from getting into biking? That same freedom you loved as a child is still out there — along with pleasant changes such as a growing number of paved bike paths, lighter weight bicycles, and multiple gear ratios which make it easy to peddle up those hills.

Perhaps you haven't noticed the change, but most cities and suburban areas now designate selected streets as preferred bike routes. You also should know that bike clubs with active programs for recreational, touring and even racing oriented senior bikers now exist in many communities. In turn, the U.S. Cycling Association has a membership of more than 20,000.

Indeed, here is a sport that has advantages for almost everyone 50-and-over. It can provide excellent conditioning, yet doesn't overstress ankles and knees. On the other hand, you can always find scenic routes where a leisurely pace is just the thing. And, with all ages participating, it can be a fun family sport (but leave your pup at home — on or off a leash, dogs are a menace to safe biking).

For a short, intensive workout, it's nice to be able to start and finish your biking right at home. Or, you can choose bike touring, adventures that offer new vistas and easy companionship. You don't have to carry your own sleeping quarters and kitchen with you when touring. Most of the places you'd care to ride through also will have bed and breakfast facilities reasonably nearby.

Now, if you can't wait to get your new bike, there's likely to be a bike shop at a neighboring shopping plaza, or you may find just what you want in the classified section of the newspaper. Whatever model you finally choose, use it! Saddle bags or a basket will fit all models, so you can combine errands with enjoyable exercise. No, don't throw away the keys to your car. Just get a rack so your bike can go with you on your next long trip.

EASE OF LEARNING

Don't laugh too hard. Of course you know how to ride a bike. Just don't count on your sense of balance being quite so sharp as in the old days. Yes, even you who used to ride around the block with no hands!

Assuming you do want the advantages of the modern, geared bicycle that provides easy pedaling going uphill and more speed with less effort on the flat (and you can choose from 3, 5, 10 and even higher geared models), means learning to use hand rather than foot brakes. You will find that one of the hand brakes acts on the rear wheel while the other controls the front wheel. A little experimenting here is time well spent, since braking with the front wheel alone can easily cause a fall. Also, withhold your urge for immediate speed. Instead, practice shifting gears up and down — something that must be done only while the bike is moving, not stopped, and should be executed smoothly, not forced.

For those who will settle just for the familiar old faithful balloon tire model, you will be happy to know that reasonable replicas are around. Better yet, the "mountain bike" has been born. Looking more like the traditional bike (yet constructed with a lighter but stronger frame), the mountain bike boasts a full range of gears that can handle almost any hill. Knobby tires improve traction but the ride remains smooth. Don't forget that your knees and legs are no longer those of that wiry 10-year-old. Try the geared models. Walking your bike up those hills may be acceptable exercise, but it isn't much fun.

Which Sports For You?

Top, the five gear sprockets on the rear wheel give this bike its five speeds. The 10-speed bike (below) has the same five gears on the rear wheel, but the drive or pedal sprocket has a high and low gear so each of the five speeds can be adjusted upwards, making a total of 10 speeds.

The simpler touring bike (top) has a single brake lever on each side of the handle bar. The bottom photo shows the combined racing/touring bike with two brake levers on each side of the handle bar. The horizontal lever is used when riding upright; the vertical lever is used when the body is bent forward and the hands are on the curved part of the handle bar.

Which Sports For You?

Balloon tires give the mountain bike its great traction, while gears provide easy pedalling.

SEASONAL LIMITATIONS

Other than snowy or icy pavements, biking is an all-season sport. While biking in the rain may occasionally be necessary, it is not recommended since both you and the bike tend to suffer. On the other hand, a clear but chilly day can be great. Don't worry. You'll be warm in short order. Clear glasses can be a big help. They'll protect against flying gravel or insects and, in nippy weather, will prevent tears from blurring your vision.

TIME EXPENDED

Biking, along with walking, can fit anyone's schedule. There is never a wasted moment getting started unless your bike is kept on a garage rack that everyone else in the family uses for a convenient catch-all or you lock your bike and lose the key. Unfortunately, geared bikes are popular items for thievery these days, so locks are a bothersome necessity.

INITIAL AND RECURRING COSTS

If you are going to take advantage of the modern and very practical gear shift model, then get a bike with a well made derailleur. This is the actual gear shifting mechanism on the rear wheel. The bottom end of the line will be around $175 and you can pay a lot more depending on the number of gears, overall bike weight and other refinements. There are some excellent buys on the second-hand market. Often you can get a much better used bike for less money than a new bike at the bottom of the price scale. Just make sure you or a friend are knowledgeable enough to ascertain a used bike's true condition.

If you don't run your bike into curbs or pot holes, leave it out in the rain, or keep shifting gears improperly, it will last a long time with very modest additional expense. New tires cost about $10 each, but you can do a lot of riding with the original set. The basic rule is to replace tires when the tread is down. That's when punctures start.

A yearly tune-up by your local bike shop costs $35-$45 and is a wise investment. The mechanically inclined may enjoy the intricacies of tensioning and adjusting the derailleur, but most of us should leave this task to the specialist. You may not like the way a helmet looks, but by all means wear one. They cost from $25 to $75, are more comfortable they they look and are vital protection.

LOCAL AND REGIONAL AVAILABILITY

Again, biking is a winner. It not only travels with you easily by car, but rental bikes can be found almost anyplace. Resorts stock them in various sizes and shapes. These usually are suitable for scenic riding but not necessarily for hard biking. Increasingly, however, bike touring packages are available at the recreational level for trips that range as short as a weekend. More information is available from Bikecentennial, P.O. Box 8303, Missoula, Montana 59807.

FITNESS LEVEL

Since biking also is recommended as a conditioning activity, it serves a wide range of fitness levels. By using a relatively low gear,

Which Sports For You?

All racks will hold two bicycles, and the rear-end model allows you to bring along an extra sport too!

SPORTS AFTER 50

The narrow seat in the top photo is better for fast paced riding. The wider seat on the touring bike (bottom photo) is more comfortable for recreational use.

Which Sports For You?

one can bicycle with minimum strain on the legs and cardiovascular system. Then, as your conditioning and fitness level improve, you can advance your energy output by using a higher gear, although care should be taken not to put too much stress on arthritic joints. Biking also is therapeutic when rehabilitating ankle, knee or hip injuries. The smooth constant motion improves flexibility and provides muscle toning, while using a lower gear in the early stages of rehabilitation will avoid over-stressing the soft tissues of joint surfaces. As long as you bike within your target pulse rate, you will be conditioning, not harming yourself.

If you haven't ridden for a while, your seat and that of the bike may not match very well. Until the former adjusts to the realities, go with the wider and softer variety. Also, to avoid possible back strain, raise the handlebars higher when starting. You won't look quite so dashing following these changes, but you will bike more comfortably. Seat height and tilt also affect biking comfort. Seat height is important and it should be adjusted so that with the pedal at the lowest part of the stroke, and your foot flat, your leg will be not quite fully extended. The seat tilt that is best for you can only be determined after you have tried a few different angles.

AEROBIC QUALITIES

Biking's deserved reputation as a conditioning activity also qualifies it as an excellent aerobic sport for those sufficiently fit. Like rowing and cross country skiing, the aerobics quality can range from low to high as the individual chooses. This is an immense advantage for the person who can only schedule one sport, since it allows the recreational biker a variety of pleasurable options.

SKILL LEVEL FOR ENJOYMENT

For anyone who has ever ridden a bike — and that fits most of us — there really are no further refinements that must be mastered. The 50-and-over person who is again taking up biking will feel at home very quickly on a modern 3, 5, or 10 speed bike. True, they

SPORTS AFTER 50

steer and balance a bit more sensitively than the old style bike, but you will adapt easily to this as well as to the hand brakes. With the advent of sophisticated three-wheel bicycles for adults, even those with rather serious physical disabilities also can enjoy this sport.

Bike touring is a decidedly pleasurable adventure. Before going on one, however, you should feel very confident in your bike handling abilities. Being able to handle uphill and downhill terrain where there is much shifting of gears, riding on narrow paths or with other riders close beside you, and making sudden stops are all part of happy touring. You don't need a special course. Just keep biking and your confidence will develop naturally.

Safety helmets *do* protect. Wear one. They are more comfortable than they look.

Which Sports For You?

INJURY POTENTIAL

If one could confine their biking totally to uncrowded bike paths, then few injuries would occur. Occasionally, however, we must bike part of the way on busy streets and also cross high traffic intersections. On a bike path, a collision with another rider might throw you, but with your helmet on, you are likely to receive only a few bruises.

On a busy street, even the helmeted biker is vulnerable. At intersections with lights, there is a temptation for the accomplished biker to use the yellow caution lights for cutting across. You may save a few minutes but the price for error is too high. For maximum safety, walk your bike across in the pedestrian lane and only on green lights. As for riding along a heavily used street, and particularly one with cars parked on the side, you are at risk from all sides: the sudden opening of a parked car's door... an overtaking car; or, if you are in the middle; a head-on hit. The only sensible alternative is to walk your bike on the sidewalk. You may feel funny and get some stares, but you will avoid the accident column.

To direct attention to their presence in traffic, some cyclists attach a small, brightly colored flag to a thin rod that extends up four or five feet above the frame. It may seem superfluous, but you are safer when a car or truck driver knows you are there.

CAN YOU DO IT ALONE?

Unless you've made the mistake of buying a bicycle built for two, you have chosen a sport that needs no partner or scheduling, yet the sport also can offer a great deal of companionship for those who so desire. And, obviously, a bicycle built for two can be great fun also.

SOCIABILITY

Whether you are touring on a bike or just riding with a friend, biking is companionable. On a bike path it is certainly quiet enough to talk back and forth, even while maintaining a fair pace, and part of the fun of touring is the shared experiences as a group. The large number of bike clubs testify to this fact. A majority of communities now have special programs for seniors, but biking, like boardsailing, is a sport where differing ages can mix effortlessly. Other than outright racing, there are few barriers. The light weight 5 or 10 speed bike is as pleasurable for women as for men, young and old. It is not a fad. Biking is here to stay!

Bike tours can be short or long, hug the valley or climb mountains. Join your local bike club and discover a new cameraderie.

ROWING/SCULLING

While sculling is a form of rowing, most persons' rowing experience is a far cry from the pleasurable sport of rowing/sculling, which uses a long, light and narrow hull, or shell, in contrast to the familiar flat-bottomed and broad-beamed rowboat. As a result, the sculler can glide through the water swiftly and gracefully instead of struggling with the stiff oar locks, rigid seat and difficult steering characteristics of the old rowboat.

A rowing shell seems to skim the surface of the water.

Although the rowing shell has been around for a long time, this kind of rowing was primarily a college and university sport with emphasis on an eight-oared shell called crew. Strong in the east, midwest and far west, the sport tended to attract tall, raw-boned athletes who trained year around for conditioning and to develop the perfect technique and teamwork for a winning crew who then pushed their bodies to the limit in four-mile races. Such extreme competition still exists, but crew as a sport has greatly expanded.

SPORTS AFTER 50

Modern composition materials produce a shell that is graceful, yet strong.

Which Sports For You?

Today, women's as well as men's lightweight crews (in two, four and eight person shells) compete in shorter length sprint events at high school, college and post-college regattas.

Interestingly, the single person shell, or sculling, was originally not so popular in the U.S., although it was a highly competitive sport in Europe. The high initial cost and upkeep expense of a shell limited single person rowing. Constructed only of selected woods and handcrafted all the way, the wooden racing shell is a fragile craft that demands great care in its use and maintenance. Three rather recent, but unrelated developments have now combined to dramatically widen rowing's appeal to all age levels.

First was the advent of fiberglass and related epoxy and composition materials for building any type of boat hull. Instead of the extremely costly wooden shell, the light hull now could be formed on a production line. And whereas the fragile wooden hull was impractical for recreational use except by an experienced oarsman, the new,

The shell's light weight makes it easy for anyone to carry.

less expensive composition shells are not so easily damaged and also are unsinkable due to flotation material under the decking.

Then, with the surge of public interest in health and fitness a few years ago came the discovery that rowing exercised more body muscles than most other sports. Indoor rowing machines, simulating the stroke, body motion and exertion levels of actual rowing, sprouted in the health and fitness clubs. Suddenly came the word: "Rowing is good for you!"

Perhaps the greatest boost for the sport emanated from the 1984 Olympics. Rowing not only was a sport that received excellent TV coverage, but the U.S. was the unexpected winner of the men's doubles sculling event. Rowing captured sport page headlines overnight. Even more important, TV close-ups of the Olympic action brought the full dynamics of this sport into millions of homes. The rhythm of the rower, the sweep of the graceful oars, and the swish of the water against the surging hull could almost be felt right through the screen. This was rowing!

The beautiful laminated wooden shells are still being made for those individuals who like to race as well as for the traditionalists who simply want the best. However, the majority of shells being constructed today are made of composition materials. Equally important, boat clubs offering programs for the recreational rower as well as for the racer are springing up around the U.S.

The composition shell, moreover, has opened up the sport for all types of recreational rowers and in particular for the 50-and-older person who is seeking an outdoor sport that can be quickly learned, enjoyed in varied weather conditions and offers a wide range of fitness benefits. The shell itself requires almost no maintenance, can be transported on a regular car rack (the new light-weight shells weigh 40 pounds or less), and is easy to launch from shore or dock.

You will see more and more of these modern rowboats skimming along our country's many lakes, rivers and bays. Try it. You are very likely to become an enthusiast too.

EASE OF LEARNING

Rowing is a relatively easy sport to learn. Most of us — at least

Which Sports For You?

those who have spent occasional vacation time near lakes or bays — may have struggled with the old, flat-bottomed rowboat. Well, sculling is rowing made truly enjoyable.

In less than an hour, someone experienced in rowing a shell can show you how to get into it, properly adjust the "foot stretcher",

The cockpit contains the sliding seat and the "stretcher" holding the foot stirrups. The stretcher can be adjusted forward or backward to accommodate differing leg lengths.

which secures the feet so one's legs can push and pull the seat along the slide, balance the shell by laying the oars flat on the water's surface, and then execute the proper stroke. It requires practice to smooth out the stroke (there is a tendency for the beginner to dip the oars too deep or too shallow or to pull unevenly, since one arm usually is stronger than the other). The rowing stroke combination of leg thrust followed by back and arm pull, and then movement of the sliding seat back again to the start position soon becomes a natural rhythm.

The shell is balanced by using one hand to keep both oars flat on the water. This allows the rower to step into the cockpit securely and also maintains the shell's stability while the rower adjusts the stirrups.

Positively, you will be off rowing your first day. But don't overdo it! Unless you have been working out on an indoor rowing machine, you will have some unused muscles that deserve consideration — particularly those in the lower back.

INITIAL AND RECURRING COSTS

There is a sizable investment in the shell, rig and oars. The complete set will run $1,500 and up for a fiberglass production model and $700 and up for a second-hand one, but this should be a one-time expense. Reasonable care will maintain the hull in good condition for many years (and an epoxy repair kit will restore punctures or cracks that might occur from grounding or hard landing against a dock.) Oars can break, however. Although these traditionally have been made of laminated wood, strong composition oars now are available. A good set of light oars is worthwhile and to replace an oar will cost $50 and up, depending on quality.

If there is a rowing club nearby, there are obvious advantages to joining, particularly if membership allows rentals. If you purchase a shell and are fortunate enough to have your own or a friend's dock available, there really are no other recurring expenses. Should you have to use a local marina, however, then some kind of a launching and storing fee probably will be necessary.

SEASONAL LIMITATIONS

The refinement of comfortable, warmth-protecting wetsuits have made rowing, along with many other sailing activities, eight and ten month sports, even in some northern climates. Rowing perhaps offers somewhat more flexibility than other forms of boating since it is ideal on those days when there is little or no wind. It also can handle a reasonable chop. Rough waves and big winds, on the other hand, can lead to swamping or capsizing, so there will be lost days for rowing, too. The indoor rowing machine, however, is always available. While not comparable in enjoyment, the indoor version is good conditioning and some machines simulate the rowing stroke quite well.

TIME EXPENDED

If you own your own shell, scheduling is up to you. If you are a member of a rowing club and need to rent a shell, you will have to schedule in advance, but it is generally possible to plan a regular schedule. In any case, other than travel time from your home or office, there is little wasted time in getting on the water. Ten or fifteen minutes is all that is necessary to put the shell in the water and rig the seat and oars.

LOCAL AND REGIONAL AVAILABILITY

If a lake, river or bay is reasonably near, it is usually possible to also find a suitable storage and launching spot. Car topping makes it quite simple and practical to travel some distance.

At present, few resorts have shells available for rental, but the growing popularity of rowing should improve this situation in the near future. Also, given the expanding number of rowing clubs around the country, arrangements can be made to enjoy the sport in other areas through cooperating memberships.

FITNESS LEVEL NEEDED

Compatibility with a wide range of fitness levels is a special attribute of this sport. One can row a shell at a slow but consistent pace that puts little stress on one's body. It also is possible to row with an intensity that fully stresses most of your body muscles as

With oars perpendicular to the cockpit and blades flat on the water, the shell is stable -- allowing the rower to rest comfortably whenever tired.

well as your cardiovascular and pulmonary systems.

Because of this flexibility, individuals with pulmonary limitations, such as moderate emphysema, can row safely and still obtain important aerobic and body conditioning. The sitting position reduces the oxygen requirement of exercise while the degree of energy expended in the rowing stroke is always controlled by the rower.

Since so many muscles throughout the body (ankles, upper and lower legs, stomach, back, shoulders, arms, wrists and fingers) are exercised, rowing can be an excellent conditioning sport for anyone.

As with other exercise that can work the body so effectively, one should start slowly and build up endurance with care. This is especially important for those who wish to row competitively. Along with the need for excellent overall fitness, racing demands a cardiovascular system without any weakness.

SKILL LEVEL FOR ENJOYMENT

Little needs to be added here that was not noted under Ease of Learning. The basic elements of the stroke do not really alter, no matter how fast or slow you row. The faster the stroke, the more precisely each element of the stroke must be executed. A smooth, powerful, but slower stroke rate will, in fact, produce more boat speed than a faster, choppier stroke of equal power.

Perhaps the most difficult piece of body coordination is at the end of the stroke, which is known as the "pull-through." The oar blades must be brought quickly out of the water and simultaneously feathered — accomplished by rotating the wrists upward to bring the oar blades parallel to the water — while sliding the seat forward into position for your next stroke.

Like many sports, rowing can be its own best teacher — once you have proper initial instruction. A mistake, for example, in feathering the oar is almost sure to grab your attention, since the blade probably will catch in the water, jerking your arm and body and, in the process, ruining a smooth recovery for the next stroke. So, row, row, row your boat is the formula for developing a good stroke, and not always in smooth water. Modest wind and wave chop can affect balance and rhythm, so you should practice in these conditions too.

SPORTS AFTER 50

The seat is forward and the arms extended as the blades enter the water at the beginning of the stroke (top). Halfway through the stroke (middle), the legs have partially extended (leg thrusts), and the arms are starting to bend for the final pull through. In the bottom photo, the stroke has been completed. The blades have been raised out of the water and have just been "feathered" in preparation to bringing the seat forward again into position for the next stroke.

Which Sports For You?

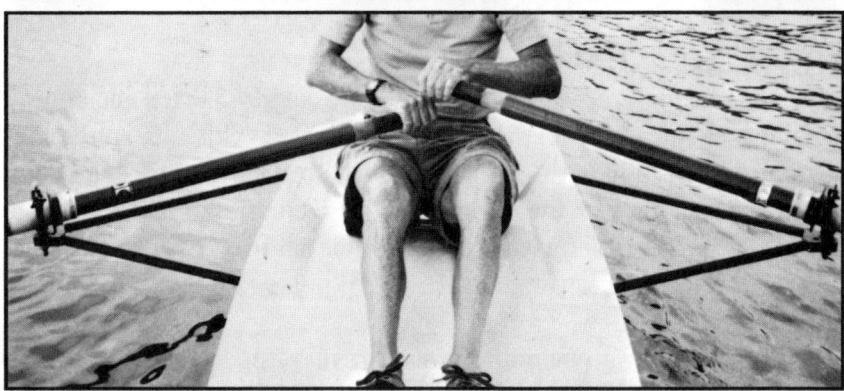

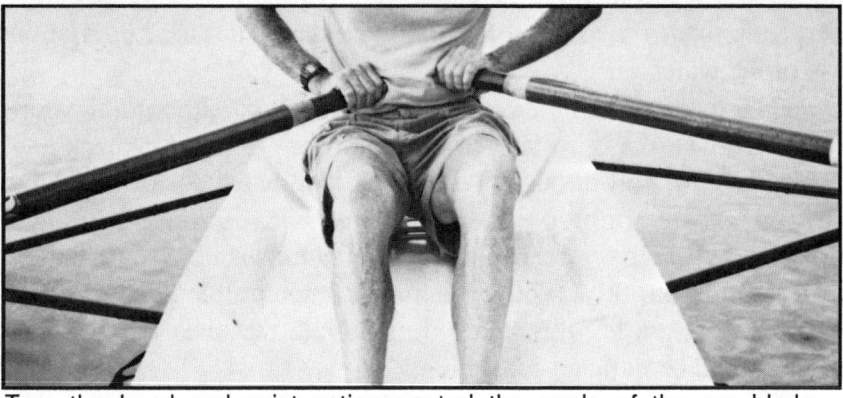

Top, the hand and wrist action control the angle of the oar blade. Here, the blades have just entered the water to commence the stroke. With most of the stroke completed (middle), the arms are well bent getting ready for the final pull through. The hands are close to their finishing position. The bottom photo shows the completed stroke, with the blades raised and feathered. Note the dropped wrists and raised knuckles -- the action which accomplishes feathering of the oars.

The aim is to develop a smooth, consistent stroke that both powers the shell forward and reinforces its momentum. The result will be a combination of power, rhythm and boat speed that is particularly satisfying.

AEROBIC QUALITIES

Rowing is one of the top all around conditioning sports, able to produce any level of aerobic training the rower is properly conditioned to experience. The sustained effort and the heavy work of the big muscle group, especially those of the arms, legs, stomach and back, make rowing an excellent activity for improving fitness.

INJURY POTENTIAL

The exercise capacity of rowing, particularly the aerobic conditioning aspect, can be very dangerous if abused. This falls under the heading of bad judgment on the part of the rower, though, and is not an inherent danger of the sport. For the recreational rower whose basic health is satisfactory, the injury potential from over-exertion is low. He or she will know the safe target pulse rate and will row at or below that level.

Also, knowing when and *how* to rest is important. When motionless, a shell remains well balanced only if both oars are extended perpendicular to the side of the shell and the blades are kept flat on top of the water.

The most vulnerable body area is the back. Although the correct rowing stroke is initiated by a strong leg push, not by back leverage, the final pull-through and the constant seated position without support, puts extra pressure on the lower back. Strong abdominal muscles will help counter this. See the exercises noted in Chapter VII. In addition, those with a history of knee problems might find that too strong a leg thrust could aggravate the knee joint, so leg drive should be initiated carefully.

One overall caution: A rowing shell sits low in the water and is not highly visible. Moreover, the rower faces backward. This combination makes you vulnerable to other boats, especially to those going excessively fast or simply expect others to keep out of their way. A small brightly colored flag similar to that used by many bicyclists will improve the shell's visibility, but nothing beats looking over your shoulder frequently.

CAN IT BE ENJOYED ALONE?

Sculling, by definition, involves a single rowed shell. There are two-person as well as four and eight-oared shells, but these are used primarily for racing. The recreational rower is in his own world.

SOCIABILITY

The above is not to say that the sport lacks sociability. True, it is very much for the individual. On the other hand, the pleasure of skimming along near a wooded shoreline or gliding silently through marsh-bordered estuaries — to be rewarded, maybe, by the icy glare of a feeding heron — offers a special kind of sociability that only nature can provide.

And rowers, like all enthusiasts enjoy sharing with others the pleasures and intricacies of their sport. Also, since one generally rows for no more than one hour at a stretch, you can relax on the shore while your partner takes a turn. Finally, if competition beckons, you will find that rowing regattas offer enjoyable socializing as well as opportunities to test and refine your skills.

RACQUET SPORTS

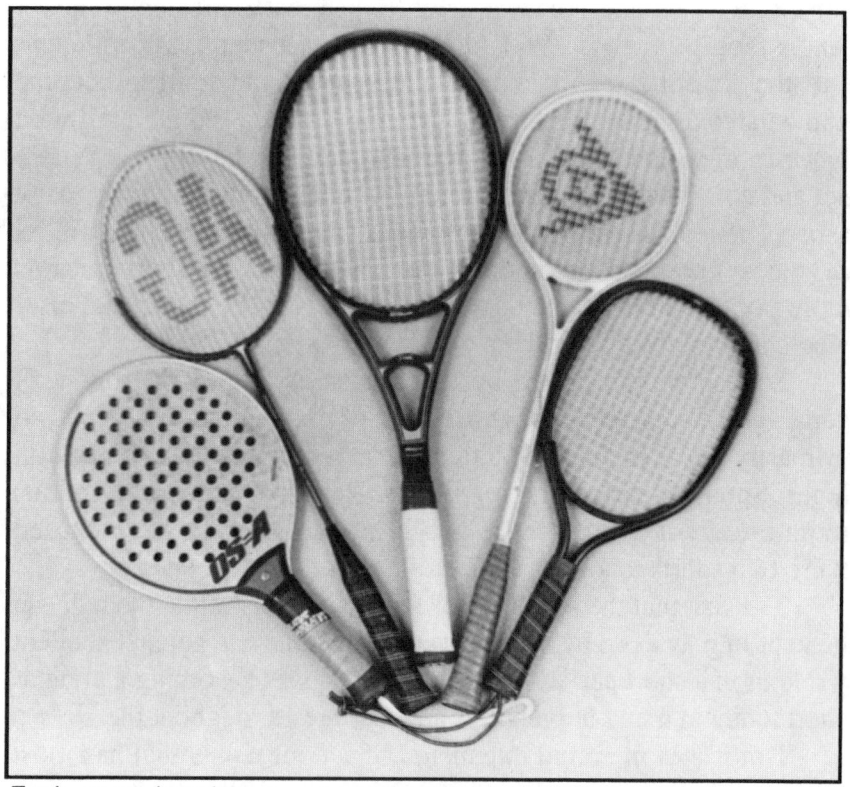

Each sport has its own racquet shape. From left are racquets for paddle tennis, badminton, tennis, squash and racquetball.

Racquet sports have been part of the American sporting scene for many years and fully deserve their tremendous national popularity. The majority of individuals 50-and-over who play one or more of these sports started with tennis and, since it is the most difficult to learn and play, many have easily adapted to the related sports of paddle tennis, squash, racquetball, and badminton. For a long time, badminton was considered only a "fun game." Recent television coverage of international competition in this sport, however, has illustrated how athletic it can be when played aggressively.

Interestingly, paddle tennis was devised in the east as a winter substitute for tennis. This was prior to the great explosion of indoor tennis facilities in the 1960s. Played on a wooden platform about half the size of a tennis court, which caused the sport to become known also as Platform Tennis, the court is enclosed by a tall wire fence from which the ball can rebound and still be in play. With a net and court layout similar to tennis, paddle tennis combines many aspects of tennis with some features of squash and racquetball. Its devotees are apt to be outdoor enthusiasts and the sport remains more popular in the Atlantic states and in New England than elsewhere around the country.

Squash was designed by the British as an indoor, four-wall game. Introduced here in the early part of this century, it was played primarily in the major U.S. cities and in a few universities and colleges. Squash's early contemporaries, Racquets and Court Tennis, require extremely expensive playing courts, which have caused these two sports to all but vanish..

The fact that the squash stroke is easy to learn, that the ball can be kept in play even by beginners, and that one can get an excellent workout in a short period has resulted in squash becoming a popular sport today in many universities and colleges throughout the U.S.

But it was the rapid expansion of indoor tennis that has most impacted the racquet sports' world. Not only did this make tennis a year around sport throughout the U.S., but with evening as well as daytime hours of play, indoor courts brought many newcomers into the game. It also kept many middle-aged and older persons playing, particularly in the east and midwest, who otherwise might well have dropped out of the sport due to its seasonal limitations.

In addition, the new tennis and racquet clubs spawned racquetball, a game more like squash than tennis, but using a racquet and ball closer in shape to the latter. Racquetball also can be learned very quickly, is fun even at the beginner's level and, like squash, can provide a relatively quick and strenuous workout. Downtown athletic clubs offering squash and racquetball are now popular in most

Which Sports For You?

Racquetball (top) and squash (bottom) courts are quite similar in overall size.

sizable cities, while indoor tennis courts (many also with racquetball courts) are fixtures of the suburbs.

Many community tennis courts provide excellent lighting for night play.

Whether it was the advent of men's and women's professional tennis competition whose star performers receive extensive television and other media coverage, the rapid development of indoor tennis facilities, or the construction of good public tennis courts in both urban and suburban communities or a combination of all three, tennis continues to dominate the other racquet sports. The United States Tennis Association (USTA) now has a membership of over 250,000 and the sport continues to boom with growing attention being paid to seniors participation.

Squash, racquetball, paddle tennis and badminton are growing in popularity, too, and also offer tournament schedules for senior players. None of these sports, however, can match the USTA's

Which Sports For You?

schedule of regional and national senior tournaments for every five year age classification, for both men and women, starting at age 35. The USTA men's senior competition tops out at 80 and older!

The 50 and older person who has never played any racquet sport, however, will find badminton, racquetball, squash or paddle tennis much easier to learn than tennis.

Still, racquet sports as a whole represent a wonderful sports avenue for individuals of many ages. With singles, doubles and mixed doubles competition, plus outdoor, indoor and public court facilities, tennis is perhaps the most complete family sport of the five, yet each offers something unique, and if you learn one, it is possible to learn and enjoy them all.

EASE OF LEARNING

Tennis is by far the most difficult of all the racquet sports to learn to play. Not only must eye/hand coordination be very good, but the beginning tennis player faces many more variables.

First, the racquet is relatively heavy and cumbersome for the beginner to swing properly. The recent development of oversize racquets with lighter, but stronger, frames have aided the beginner by increasing the ball contact area and facilitating racquet control. Nevertheless, it still takes time and patience just to learn the different strokes.

The basic forehand and backhand strokes are executed quite differently for the volley, half volley or ground stroke. In turn, the serve and overhead smash require a completely different stroke motion and body movement.

At the same time, the ball's flight and bounce must be judged correctly to get into position to hit the ball back over the net and into the opponent's court. Different court surfaces such as clay, Har-tru, cement and several types of indoor coverings, alter bounce and speed of the ball as does the type of stroke one's opponent has used (slice, cut, top spin, or flat). Wind velocity and direction also affect the ball's bounce and speed, a factor that makes indoor tennis particularly attractive.

For all the above reasons, professional instruction is strongly recommended. While it is possible to use incorrect strokes and still

Good instruction includes explanation and discussion along with demonstration. This is particularly important in learning the different tactics and court positions required in tennis doubles.

hit the ball back, particularly with the new larger racquet, this is apt to be costly in three ways: 1. Poor strokes become ingrained and thus handicap improvement of skills; 2. Bad habits are difficult to break later; 3. Improper strokes frequently lead to injuries.

In contrast, Badminton, which is normally played indoors, probably is the easiest racquet sport to learn. Hand/eye coordination still is necessary, but the slower moving bird, or shuttlecock, is an easier target to meet. The fact that the bird is always struck while in the air (no bounce is allowed) eliminates most other variables. Although the small size of the racquet head is, at first, a handicap in making contact with the bird, the racquet is very light and can be swung effectively with a natural and easy wrist motion. This makes timing the stroke much simpler and also allows the stroke to be made almost regardless of foot or body position.

Which Sports For You?

The lively ball and allowable play against all four walls and the ceiling, keeps racquetball players in almost constant motion.

Squash and racquetball are roughly comparable to each other from a learning difficulty standpoint, with both being far easier than tennis, but more complex than badminton. Each requires learning the angles, that is, the way the ball bounces off the walls under differing spins. On the other hand, unlike tennis, you frequently get a second chance, especially in racquetball, if the ball gets by you because ball speed often makes it carom off another wall allowing you to still hit it (as long as it has not bounced twice).

Also, there is no net. Striking the ball so it reaches the large front wall on the fly is all that is necessary to keep it in play. Squash courts, however, have an 18-inch-high metal cover along the base of the front wall, and the point is lost if the ball strikes this. In both sports, the racquets and racquet heads are smaller and lighter than a tennis racquet. The strokes, made with the forearm and wrist rather

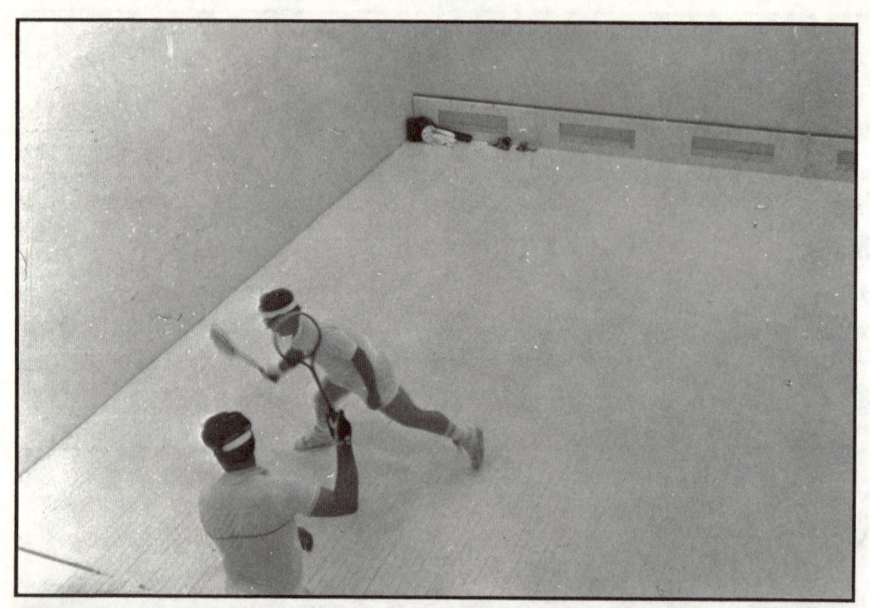

Squash (top) with its 18-inch error zone on the front wall, a six-foot maximum height allowable on the back wall and no play against the ceiling, is more structured than racquetball, but just as fast. (Bottom) Paddle tennis provides plenty of action in its constant volleying and net play.

than the full arm, shoulder and body turn of the tennis stroke, are simpler to execute. The squash stroke, because of the much longer racquet handle, requires more precise footwork and body coordination than racquetball.

Paddle tennis has many less variables than tennis. It is played primarily as doubles or mixed doubles, and uses a much smaller court. Since the action is mostly at net, entails fewer stroke variations overall and the court has just one standard playing surface, paddle tennis is considerably easier to learn than tennis.

SEASONAL LIMITATIONS

None of the racquet sports are handicapped in this respect. Indoor tennis facilities continue to expand and squash, racquetball and badminton are played indoors in any case. Badminton courts easily can be set up on the lawn, but any wind makes the game virtually impossible to play. Paddle tennis courts have been designed to make all-weather play possible. Court surfaces are relatively non-skid and movable lower sideboards make shoveling off snow a simple matter, hence play is possible even after a severe winter storm. Hat and gloves may be required on really freezing days, but the fast pace of this game generally keeps the players warm enough to shed that extra sweater.

INITIAL AND RECURRING COSTS

Initial costs for racquet sports are small. Due to the many free public courts available, tennis has the advantage over squash and racquetball in good weather as regards recurring costs, although tennis balls wear out faster than those use in the latter two sports. Many tennis players, however, prefer to play at the more comfortable facilities provided by tennis clubs and/or indoor courts. These are a necessity, in any case, for all season play and the annual dues can run from $250 to $500 and more.

For squash and racquetball, there is always a court fee. Even playing just once a week, annual costs can be $150 or more. Badminton is the least costly. Generally, there is a small fee for renting the floor space and the badminton players will have to supply the net and stanchions, which cost between $75 and $150 for an indoor set. The majority of paddle tennis courts are privately owned. Where courts are provided by tennis or other clubs, the annual dues will be comparable.

A tennis racquet should be restrung once a year, but should last an average player three to six years. Racquetball racquets are quite strong, but can break if they hit the wall too hard. Wooden laminated squash racquets are relatively fragile, but the new composition racquets don't easily break and normally last well. The badminton racquet is the most fragile, yet lasts very well because the shuttlecock is so light. Paddle tennis racquets are extremely rugged. Rather than a frame with gut or nylon strings, the paddle tennis racquet is what the game's name implies, a paddle that is made of laminated wood or composition materials throughout the handle and head.

Every tennis club and almost every indoor tennis facility will employ or have available a professional. If racquetball and/or squash is played there too, the professional will be able to instruct in that sport also. Universities that have squash facilities usually also have coaches. Badminton and paddle tennis, on the other hand, are not played so widely, and these sports are generally learned through other, more skilled players.

INSTRUCTION, RACQUET AND STRINGING EXPENSES

    Instruction
        Individual: $20-$40 per half hour
        Clinics: $10 and up per hour, depending on the number of participants
    Racquets
        Tennis: $30-$200 plus
        Racquetball: $20-$50 plus
        Squash: $25-$50 plus
        Badminton: $15-$30
        Paddle Tennis: $25-$50
    Stringing
        Tennis: $15-$30 depending on type of strings
        Squash/racquetball: $15-$20
        Badminton $10-$15

TIME EXPENDED

There is no question that racquetball and squash are preferable for the person seeking a fast workout. Thirty minutes of either sport is apt to be the equivalent of one hour of tennis. Badminton, too, can be played at a very fast pace, but also easily fits a slower rate of play. Paddle tennis doubles, with its small court and rebounding wire walls, also is likely to be a faster paced game than tennis doubles (for average players).

From the standpoint of learning time, and that includes learning the necessary strokes, tactics of the game and reaching a playing level that is enjoyable as well as good exercise, racquetball, squash, badminton and paddle tennis all offer distinct advantages over tennis.

During the busiest periods seasonally, it is usually necessary to schedule indoor tennis, racquetball and squash well in advance. In some places, the one hour playing time normally scheduled for tennis singles, and one and a half hours for doubles, are sold on a full season basis during the winter, spring and fall months. Squash and racquetball are popular lunchtime sports and will be scheduled tightly then as well as late afternoon and early evening hours.

REGIONAL AVAILABILITY

Racquet sport interest is so widespread throughout the U.S. that one can travel to almost any community and find at least a few public tennis courts. Indoor tennis and racquetball facilities also are likely to be nearby. Squash, however, normally will be limited to major cities, although some universities and colleges will allow local community use of their squash facilities.

Racquet sports equipment is easy to take along when traveling and there are few resorts in the U.S. today, or around the world, for that matter, that do not offer excellent tennis facilities. These generally will include competent professional instruction, clinics and even arranged games for visitors. Since racquetball and squash are indoor sports, however, only some of the larger resorts provide them. Indoor badminton is played wherever there are enthusiasts in the community and court arrangements usually are made with the local high school, junior college or community center for time on a space available basis. The widest interest in this sport is found in New England, New York and Michigan.

During the winter months, indoor tennis facilities are apt to be busy from early morning until late evening.

Similarly, because paddle tennis is predominantly a cold weather game primarily played in the Atlantic and midwest regions, this sport is rarely available at resorts. It usually requires personal contacts to arrange play in other parts of the country.

FITNESS LEVEL FOR PLAYING

The majority of tennis players 50-and-over primarily play doubles, thus roughly cutting in half the amount of court to be covered and the number of strokes needed. The overall physical exertion in doubles, accordingly, is not so high as in singles. Even in doubles, however, the start and stop movements, serve and overhead strokes can be dangerous exertion for the player with a weak cardiovascular system.

While one hour of tennis singles provides significant exercise for legs, trunk, shoulders and arms, it is less effective in providing aerobic conditioning because the heart rate increase is not sustained during play.

Although the exertion level remains much the same regardless

Which Sports For You?

The constant stretching, changing direction, start and stop action of racquetball (top) and squash (bottom) put a premium on strong ankles and knees.

SPORTS AFTER 50

of the court surface, the stress on angles and knees alters depending upon the playing surface. Clay and Har-tru offer the least stress; cement and indoor artificial surfaces generate the most.

Squash and racquetball are mostly played as singles. They are fast paced games requiring quick movements throughout the body, including lunging and stretching and constantly changing footwork. Although both of these sports can be played at a slower pace by beginners, inevitably, as more skill is achieved, the pace will speed up, so good aerobic fitness becomes an increasing requirement.

Badminton can be played at a slow or fast pace, singles or doubles. This offers considerable flexibility for the person 50-and-over who is just learning this sport. The degree of physical exertion expended in badminton is more easily controllable than in racquetball or squash, so the tendency towards over-exertion is minimized.

Paddle tennis, although almost always played as doubles recreationally, also is fast paced with quick changes of direction, numerous starts and stops, and considerable lunging to "dig the ball off the wire."

Since the ball is allowed to come off the screen surrounding a paddle tennis court and still remain in play, fast footwork and quick hand/eye coordination is needed in this sport too.

Which Sports For You?

Overall, then, playing racquet sports requires constant attention to sound conditioning. As a rule of thumb, warming up exercises prior to playing are always advisable. In addition, strengthening and stretching exercises for leg, ankle and arm muscles, as well as exercises to tone up the stomach muscles to protect the lower back, also are recommended.

SKILL LEVEL FOR ENJOYMENT

The numerous variables affecting tennis play not only complicate the learning process, but also force considerable practice and skill development in order to reach a playing level that is really enjoyable. Practice with a ball machine that automatically shoots balls over the net at differing speeds and heights, or hitting against a backboard, help speed up the learning process as long as good instruction has first developed a satisfactory stroke. Once a player has achieved average skills both in singles and in doubles, tennis offers a lifetime of sport and pleasure. Indeed, the many variables that increase the learning difficulty also contribute immensely to making tennis a constant and rewarding challenge for the competitive person.

Racquetball and squash, on the other hand, provide fun at an early stage of learning, with the larger racquet head and bigger ball of racquetball making it the easier of the two to learn. Both sports allow one to practice alone learning the court's angles and the way the ball bounces off the walls. The stroke is predominantly forearm and wrist (perhaps even more so in squash) and, with the large front wall as the broad target, the stroke in these two sports demands far less accuracy than in tennis. In brief, the player's skill level can improve rapidly and enjoyable competition can begin shortly after commencing these sports. Nevertheless, squash, with its 18" error zone at the bottom of the front wall, a 6-foot maximum height line across the back wall, and with the ceiling out of play, requires more precise strokes than racquetball.

Anyone who has seen badminton played at top levels knows how fast that odd looking bird can travel, how varied are the shots and how athletic the competitors must be! An attractive quality of

SPORTS AFTER 50

There is no short cut to developing tennis skills. Each basic stroke has fundamentals and variations that must be learned correctly and then practiced. Professional instruction is indispensable in learning the correct stroke. Practice and competition can then develop the consistency and confidence needed for steady improvement.

this sport, however, is the range of play satisfaction, since the sport also can be thoroughly enjoyed at a much lower level of skill. Thus, badminton becomes a fun sport for the 50-and-older person who may not be particularly athletic but would like a sport that can provide enjoyable exercise. As in tennis, there is much less physical exertion in doubles than in singles, but even the latter can be played without undue stress. For the novice, the slower pace of the bird's flight puts less demand on depth perception, hand/eye coordination and quick body movement. The emphasis on wrist rather than arm action makes the bird quite easy to hit even with faulty strokes. The result is a fun sport that fosters interesting competition at all levels of play.

There are few paddle tennis players who were not originally tennis players. Suffice it to say that with this background, plus the fact that it is played primarily in the cold weather months, paddle tennis may be less likely to appeal to someone who has never played a racquet sport. With average tennis playing skill, however, the shift to paddle tennis is easy, and it is a fun and competitive sport for those who prefer outdoor exercise throughout the year.

CAN YOU ENJOY IT ALONE?

All racquet sports, obviously, are designed for competition and thus require opponents to be played. Some of them, as noted previously, can be informally practiced alone.

For tennis players primarily interested in doubles, the scheduling of matches requires considerable advanced planning. Interestingly, many confirmed doubles players seek out the proliferating adult tennis camps more as opportunities for intensive tennis playing vacations than for the emphasis on skill improvement. Overall, the increasing number of public tennis courts, and the rapid growth of city leagues, have been a boon for tennis doubles enthusiasts.

INJURY POTENTIAL

While racquet sports normally do not generate serious injuries, assuming players are reasonably well conditioned, there are several types of injuries that occur more frequently for the 50-and-older player in some of these sports.

The most common probably is "tennis elbow," a rather painful tendonitis that can afflict tennis players of all ages. It is curable with rest and proper rehabilitation. This emphasizes corrective strengthening exercises for the arm, wrist and fingers and includes altering the diameter of the racquet grip and, sometimes, even changing the racquet. Tennis elbow often is the result of faulty strokes, however, and unless these are corrected too, it will likely become a recurring nuisance. Shoulders also are vulnerable to painful tendonitis and bursitis.

Then there are the ankle and knee injuries fostered by the hard and unforgiving surfaces of cement and/or indoor courts. These injuries also can be successfully rehabilitated, but ankles and knees will remain vulnerable while playing on those particular surfaces.

Racquetball and squash can be hard on lower backs as well as on ankles and knees. The bounce is low, the player is constantly bending down and there is a tendency to over-swing from a crouched position. In turn, ankles and knees are stressed both by the unyielding court surface and the quick footwork the game requires.

Badminton has a low injury potential, but again, fast paced singles on the typical hardwood gym floor will stress ankles and knees. The wrist stroke, light racquet and almost weightless bird nearly eliminate arm and back injuries.

The wooden or composition racquets used in paddle tennis can sometimes also induce tennis elbow or shoulder pain. Hitting with power is not a prerequisite and a sliced or cut shot can be equally effective. Although the non-skid wooden playing surface can test ankles and knees, the springiness of the platform reduces chances of injuring those joints.

In general, conditioning exercises for the ankles and knees are particularly advisable for anyone 50-and-over commencing racquet sports. In addition, those who have a history of ankle, knee and/or back problems should have these areas medically checked before getting started in the racquet sports. Often, equipment modification and/or corrective exercises, will enable you to play without further endangering those problem areas.

Which Sports For You?

Finally, the court confinement for racquetball and squash necessitate that players stroke the ball with a minimum "follow-through" in order to avoid hitting their opponent with the racquet. In addition, those who wear glasses need protective type glasses.

AEROBIC QUALITIES

Each of the racquet sports can offer aerobic qualities in singles. Racquetball and squash perhaps develop the most because they are played so intensively in a small court and, with a small ball that is hit hard, require quicker reflexes and faster footwork. For those who are sufficiently fit to handle intensive aerobic conditioning, racquetball or squash played for a 45-minute period three times a week will provide such benefits.

If tennis singles is played without resting between sets, then several sets of tennis, three times weekly, would achieve roughly the same aerobic benefit as the above. The time delay between points and in changing courts, however, reduces the aerobic condition quality of tennis.

Obviously, badminton singles played at a high skill level also provides excellent aerobics and this would apply as well to paddle tennis singles. None of the racquet sports, however, would provide significant aerobic conditioning in doubles.

SOCIABILITY

Singles play in all racquet sports tends to foster the strongest competitiveness. Opponents need to be fairly equal in skill and conditioning for the game to be enjoyable competition.

Tennis doubles is considerably less intensive and mixed doubles is clearly a more social sport that has been gaining in popularity. In fact, the development of indoor tennis courts has generated occasional social evenings during which a group of mixed doubles teams will have reserved courts for round robin matches between the teams, all of which are scheduled in conjunction with casual refreshments and buffet.

Tennis clubs also try to encourage competition, since such matches not only improve individual skills, but also foster an active club ranking ladder. At the same time, most clubs also promote social events to broaden membership interest. This combination of competitive outlet and enjoyable social functions works well for those who like to mix these two activities.

Doubles and mixed doubles continue to grow in popularity for badminton and paddle tennis as well as for tennis. The physical space limitations of squash and racquetball courts have prevented growth of doubles in these two sports. Racquetball doubles is played in the same court as singles. In squash, the relatively long squash racquet demands considerable swinging room and a separate larger court is necessary for this sport, which limits availability.

CANOEING

Canoeing surely is an American original, for it was developed by our continent's first settler, the Indian, and provided him with critical transportation along the rivers and lakes so vital to his existence. How extraordinary that his skillful, efficient design, serving the single canoeist as well as two or more, never has been significantly altered. Although fiberglass now has replaced the original birchbark construction, the same smooth lines, light frame weight, impressive load capacity and extremely shallow draft have all remained unchanged.

If fascination with canoeing extends back to our nation's early history, today's lively interest in this sport is properly due to the canoe's exceptional versatility. While synthetic construction materials have made the canoe tough, light and easily car topped, young and old enthusiasts alike are discovering or re-discovering how practical and pleasurable the canoe can be. It serves the nature lover, the camper and the fisherman while providing a healthy and vigorous form of exercise and sport for anyone. With leeboards, it can even be rigged as a light sailboat and in shallow estuaries, tidal marshes and winding rivers, nothing matches a canoe for easy and enjoyable transportation.

Although relatively unstable in unskilled hands, it can safely ride out rough water under the control of an experienced canoeist. Learning is quite easy and even a novice can become a safe canoeist within a relatively short period. For those who master the canoe's versatility and the techniques to control it, fast running rivers and turbulent rapids offer exciting and challenging adventure.

Fortunately, today's resurging interest in preserving the vitality of our country's thousands of lakes and rivers also is expanding the opportunities for this wonderful sport. Organizations like the Connecticut River Watershed Council (CRWC), founded in 1952 to, "Promote the protection and wise use of the Connecticut River Valley's natural resources," also are flourishing in other regions of our country. These organizations serve a critical function by keeping our waterways open and safe for public enjoyment and the American Canoe Association works closely with them.

All these regional organizations realize that canoeists are generally excellent users of our waterways, and disturb neither the quality of the water nor the surrounding environment. The CRWC, among its other important concerns, also sponsors a regular series of canoe trips from June through mid-October. Many are overnight, others purely day trips, but all with experienced guides. Although CRWC provides canoes, they also encourage participants to bring their own canoes and to share the educational and fun experience with newcomers. Comparable programs in other regions also support and promote the advantages of canoeing.

So, here is another sport for the entire family or just for you alone. As with biking, however, the family dog should not be invited. Try canoeing. See how quickly you can learn the fundamentals and enjoy the good exercise and many pleasures it offers.

EASE OF LEARNING

There are two vital but rather easy learning experiences important to canoeing. One is getting in or out while keeping the canoe balanced, but executed differently for a single canoeist than if one or more passengers are involved. The other is learning to use the paddle for stability as well as for power and steering.

When canoeing alone, you sit on the front seat or thwart facing back toward the rear of the canoe or kneel between the seat and the center thwart. This puts your weight on a wider section of the canoe, which provides better lateral stability and keeps the canoe more level in the water. Being double ended, the boat moves equally well in either direction.

To get in, the single canoeist places one hand on the far gun-

Which Sports For You?

Left: With a hand on each gunwale, the canoeist steps in. Right: Keeping his weight on the center line of the canoe to maintain its stability, the single canoeist gets ready to kneel on the flooring.

wale (rail) of the canoe and the other hand on the near side rail, steps into the canoe on the center line of the flooring and then sits on the seat, or kneels. Exiting is done in reverse, but, again, with emphasis on keeping one's weight well centered while getting up.

With two persons, the more experienced sits in the rear seat, with the passenger on the front seat facing forward. The canoe is now kept level in the water by the evenly distributed weight of both, while the more experienced of the two is better able to control and steer from the rear.

To get in when there will be one or more passengers, the experienced canoeist holds the canoe steady while the first passenger steps in and sits in the front seat facing forward. If there is another passenger, this person sits on the flooring in the middle section of the canoe. The experienced canoeist gets in last. When landing, the experienced person in the rear seat gets out first and holds the canoe steady for the passengers to exit.

Yes, a canoe is unstable, but only until the paddle is in the water. Once you become familiar with controlling the paddle, you will realize how stable a canoe can be, even in rough water. Since the paddle is the key balancing mechanism as well as the steering and means of propulsion, learning to use it correctly is important. It also is an easy and natural motion.

Grasp the paddle with one hand just above the blade (place the

SPORTS AFTER 50

right hand there if you intend to paddle on the right side; and left hand there for the left side) and place the other hand on or near the top of the paddle. Now put the blade into the water. Experiment by pulling it back and forth, then push it away from the side of the canoe and pull it back again. Feel how the canoe responds to every motion of the paddle and at the same time is steadied by the paddle's action against the water.

Left: With a passenger, the more experienced canoeist gets in first, sits on the rear seat and holds the canoe steady while his partner steps in. Right: Note that she also has a hand on each gunwale for balance and keeps her feet on the center line as she sits down on the forward seat.

Left: The order is reversed in getting out, allowing the canoe to be held steady while the less experienced canoeist gets out first. Right: She then holds the canoe steady for her partner's exit.

Which Sports For You?

Now try paddling. Keep the paddle clear of the water, extend your arms fully forward, dip the blade back into the water and simply pull you arm back towards your body. At the end of the stroke, edge the blade by turning it sideways and pressing it away from or towards the canoe. Notice how this steers the canoe either left or right while the momentum of your stroke keeps the canoe gliding forward. If you reverse the stroke by pushing the blade forward from the point where you normally finish, the canoe moves backward. Try paddling for a while, getting into the rhythm by keeping the stroke a smooth motion. Notice, too, that one can paddle on either side of the canoe, thus alternatively exercising and resting the shoulder, back and arm muscles for each side of the body.

TIME EXPENDED

As with sculling (rowing a shell), there is little wasted time in canoeing. It is a quick task to load and unload a canoe from your car rack and usually you can park reasonably near your launching spot and be on your way. The canoe enthusiast living far from boating water is obviously more limited. The majority, however, can find canoeing water within weekend travel distance.

With the paddle blade parallel to the side of the canoe, the canoe now becomes extremely stable.

SPORTS AFTER 50

Commencing the stroke.

Pulling the blade through the water.

Using the blade as a rudder to steer the canoe.

Keeping one gunwale of the canoe balanced on the car rack, the canoeist starts to roll the canoe toward his shoulder for unloading.

The center thwart now rests on his shoulders, bearing most of the canoe's weight and allowing his hands to adjust overall balance.

Which Sports For You?

COST

The least expensive way to commence canoeing is to rent. The price will vary between $15 and $25 per day, depending upon the condition and type of canoe. Most individuals who start canoeing, however, soon want the quality and variety of locations that is assured by owning their own.

This purchase should be a one-time investment, unless you eventually get into white water canoeing. The running of rapids under adverse conditions can seriously damage — if not destroy — a canoe.

A sound and very serviceable used canoe can be obtained for between $150 and $300, while a new boat will be $500 plus, depending upon its construction. Fiberglass composition materials or aluminum are most commonly used to make canoes today. Other than an occasional broken paddle, there is very little additional maintenance expense. A replacement paddle can cost $25 and up. You should always carry a spare with you, something you will do for certain after the experience of trying to paddle home with a broken one!

REGIONAL AVAILABILITY

The canoe's ability to float and navigate easily in extremely shallow water opens up many possibilities that are closed to other small boats. Low tidal waters, shoaling estuaries and small, winding rivers can readily accommodate the canoeist.

In turn, since two or more canoes can easily fit most car racks, the canoe is excellent water transportation for the many fishing and camping areas that abound throughout the country. At the same time, most lakeside or shoreline vacation facilities either will offer canoes for rent or will have access to nearby rental shops.

SEASONAL LIMITATIONS

Canoeing, as with all boating sports, faces certain cold weather limitations, yet some of the most exhilarating conditions can be found in the fall and early spring. Proper inner and outer garments are important. If you are canoeing primarily for exercise, you need

SPORTS AFTER 50

windbreaking more than heat retaining clothes since your body will be generating plenty of warmth. On the other hand, when canoeing in cold water conditions (and anything under 65 degrees fits that description) wear a wetsuit, even if the air temperature is considerably higher. This basic protection against dangerous hypothermia can be critical should you happen to capsize.

The wise canoeist also brings along a poncho or similar outer garment for that sudden rain storm. Even in summer weather, storms can produce cool and windy conditions that are a dangerous invitation to hypothermia, particularly if your clothes are wet.

SKILL LEVEL FOR ENJOYMENT

Perhaps the most serious obstacle to any beginner's enjoyment of canoeing is the initial feeling of precarious balance engendered when getting into a canoe for the first time. The canoe becomes stable once the blade is in the water. As soon as the beginner understands this concept and realizes that he or she really can control the canoe's balance, the rest comes easily. Normally, a canoe responds best to gentle and smooth movements of the paddle. The stroke,

Pushing the blade away from the side of the canoe forces the end of the canoe to turn.

even when paddling strenuously, remains a smooth and natural arm motion. The paddling rhythm itself is enjoyable. As your skill advances and you become more experienced and knowledgeable about different kinds of water conditions, you will need additional techniques to canoe well. For example, when canoeing alone into a heavy wind, it is necessary to kneel in the center section of the boat. Otherwise it will be very difficult to keep the canoe going into the wind.

Especially advanced techniques are a requirement before attempting fast running rivers with rapids. While this is one of the most exhilarating of sports, it is not for the novice. Yet anyone can learn the right techniques. The key, as always, is correct use of the paddle and your weight.

FITNESS LEVEL

Like most of the sports reviewed here, canoeing can provide varying levels of conditioning exercise. The wrists, arms, shoulders and back are the musculo-skeletal areas most affected, although the kneeling position required for canoeing alone in stronger winds will fully exercise both the upper legs and stomach muscles. Needless to add, a strong, consistent paddling stroke also will exercise the cardiovascular system.

By using a smooth easy stroke and resting occasionally, the beginning canoeist can avoid fatigue and muscle stress. Then, by lengthening the paddling periods and slowly increasing the number of strokes per minute, one can build up to more intensive workouts or be prepared to handle longer, steadily paced canoe trips.

AEROBIC QUALITY

Canoeing primarily exercises the upper body. Since intensive paddling can demand high aerobic conditioning, care should be taken in developing endurance. For most individuals, paddling at a slower pace and for a longer period is the preferable way to seek aerobic conditioning.

INJURY POTENTIAL

If one eliminates judgmental errors — and these include failure

As the canoe gathers momentum, a skillful canoeist will lean into the stroke (top left), pulling the blade through smoothly (top right), while steering to keep the canoe on course (bottom left), and using back, arms and wrists to power the stroke (bottom right).

to note adverse weather forecasts, overloading the canoe, attempting to canoe in water conditions beyond one's competence, neglecting to bring protective clothing, — the injury potential is very low.

Yes, the lower back is vulnerable to the paddling stroke, but can be protected if the canoeist strengthens the stomach muscles and then depends more on these and less on the back in executing the stroke.

Most of us have a stronger side to our body, depending on

whether we are right or left handed. There is an advantage to paddling on alternate sides of the canoe, since one can rest each side's set of muscles and also paddle in a way to build up the weaker side of the body.

Almost every canoe constructed today has flotation built into it. A few older ones may not, so take time to see that flotation material is firmly secured inside the boat. Even more important, no matter how good a swimmer you are, one life jacket for each passenger should always be on board.

CAN IT BE ENJOYED ALONE?

Canoeing can be as pleasurable alone as with a partner. Steering is perhaps easier with two, but also requires coordination between the two paddlers. An accomplished canoeing partner can be particularly helpful, however, when paddling in a stiff wind. On the other hand, single handed canoeing has its own charm and can be superior as a fitness conditioning activity.

SOCIABILITY

Canoeing offers certain unique qualities here. It doesn't require a partner, yet can provide rewarding companionship for any two individuals who enjoy the outdoors. Unlike most sports activities simultaneously involving several persons, canoeing allows easy conversation, but also time to look around, even when paddling hard, and appreciate the changing scene. As your canoe glides noiselessly along a stream or marshy estuary, you may meet a surprising amount of bird and animal life, so bring along your field glasses and camera. You may capture much more than you expected.

SPORTS AFTER 50

Two canoes can ride on a car rack as easily as one.

SKIING
ALPINE AND CROSS COUNTRY

One of the largest skiing resorts in the U.S. recently concluded that, "The biggest untapped new market" is among the seniors. That, in itself, is not so surprising since our age group is expanding more rapidly than any other. Of more interest is the less publicized fact that cross country skiing has been capturing devotees of all ages and, in particular, is making inroads into the alpine, or downhill, skiing fraternity.

For many skiers, it always has been an either/or proposition. They do alpine or cross country; yet there is no reason why one can't enjoy both branches of this same basic sport. Each inevitably has developed a distinct personality. Alpine skiing always has been the glamour sport, or so it has been promoted, and also has been considered more difficult and riskier. Cross country skiing, in turn, has been portrayed as a sport for the purist — something for the hardy, outdoor person, the individualist who likes trampling through the snow.

Although both descriptions are partially correct, they are not especially accurate or helpful to the person 50-and-over who might want to try either or both of these pleasurable activities.

There are similarities that are worth noting. Both are quite easy to learn, although the gliding motion of cross country skiing is the easiest to execute. Both demand conditioning to perform enjoyably, but cross country has the advantage of being a conditioning exercise in itself. Above all, each generates a unique and joyous rhythm, a workout that, at the end of the day, will leave the skier tired but exuberant. The separate way these two sports developed in the U.S. has influenced their different appeal.

Alpine skiing is a mountain sport that originated in the European Alps with their relatively open terrain. The steeper and more wooded mountains in the U.S. required the cutting of trails to open up ski areas. Creating and maintaining such trails, building and operating the sophisticated lifts needed to move skiers up the mountain, and providing the extensive support facilities necessary to accommodate them at the mountain base, required a huge operating complex. Thus, the ski industry was born. Capital investment was and is tremendous and necessarily has resulted in an expensive sport.

Cross country skiing, on the other hand, needs little direct support. While it is nice to ski a well marked area with nearby lodges, none of this is really necessary. It often is more fun to make one's own trail, slicing through a thinning forest or gliding across an open field. Cross country existed before the modern ski resort was conceived. Today, there are a few resorts that specialize in cross country, but these are small family run operations for the most part. Increasingly though, major alpine skiing resorts are starting to develop and promote their cross country trails. In turn, advanced cross country skiers are now seeking the challenge of mountain terrain.

Considering the above, it is easy to see why these two kinds of skiing initially attracted different types of enthusiasts, but there is no reason they should remain mutually exclusive. If you can do one, you can do the other, except those who, for medical reasons, must avoid the higher altitude (4,000 feet and over) of most alpine skiing.

You may find one more appealing than the other, but newcomers to the world of skiing should try both. We think many of you will find they happily complement each other.

EASE OF LEARNING

The alpine skier clearly faces new concepts along with some unfamiliar body positions in the learning process. The boots not only are stiff and heavy, but the bindings secure them rigidly to the skis. Years ago, this made a fearful and awesome first step for the beginner since the skis were so heavy, long and seemingly unman-

Which Sports For You?

ageable. Today's short, light skis, however, have changed all this. You quickly will find that the rigid boot/ski connection makes a good platform for balance and also provides a secure base for controlling your skis.

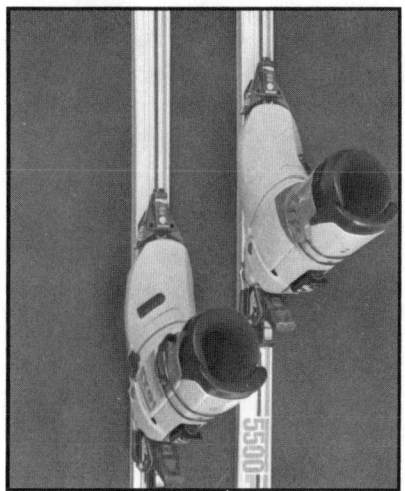

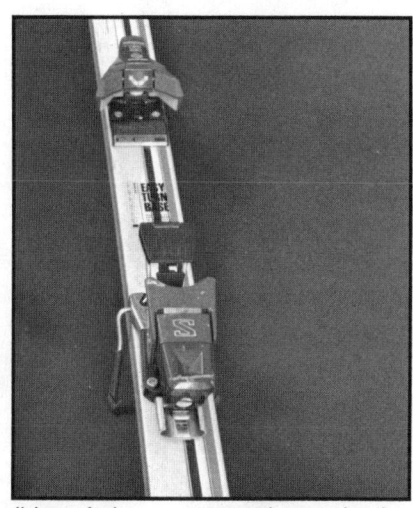

The alpine skiing boot is *not* for walking. It is constructed to grip the foot and ankle firmly, but allow the lower leg to bend forward slightly. Right: The binding is a very sophisticated mechanism, strong enough to hold the boot rigidly to the ski under all normal pressures of skiing, but sensitive enough to release the boot if too much twisting or other pressure is applied.

If you are wise, you will put yourself in the hands of a competent ski school for proper instruction (that nice little hill behind your home is not the place to learn alpine skiing; let the sledders have it). Today's professional teaching techniques are sure and safe. Your ski school instructor is skilled and knows all the techniques and steps that will quickly and safely get you skiing. Yes, alpine skiing is a humbling experience in the beginning, but at your moment of worst despair, stop to take a look around. All those individuals whizzing by you so nonchalantly also had beginnings like yours!

All of a sudden, though, you begin to feel more comfortable. Balance seems easier and you find yourself sliding nicely down a small knoll and coming to a stop. Accomplishing this a few times shows that you and your skis are starting to work together. So, don't be surprised when your instructor now shows you how to

Riding a cable car is a thrill on its own and offers spectacular mountain views. It is also the quickest way to the top of the mountain.

"stem" one or both skis and shift your weight to control directions and speed. We guarantee that the first time you do this successfully you will be hooked!

There is more to learn, to be sure, but now you are practicing movements that give you control — the key to advancing skiing skill. If you never have been on a ski lift, your instructor will show you how to get on and off, and assist you, if necessary, the first few times. You will practice this, too, on a beginner's slope and after a few trips, you will be riding the lifts with confidence.

Chair lifts normally serve differing sections of a mountain, providing access to trails designed for specific skill levels. Cable cars, on the other hand, generally run from the bottom to the top of the mountain and offer the good skier the widest choice of trails as well

Which Sports For You?

Getting off the chair lift is easy. You simply stand up and ski down the small incline that levels out after a few feet.

as the quickest way to the mountain top.

At most resorts, the ski school offers a five-day package. You will not be an accomplished skier at the end of that period, but you should be a safe and competent beginning skier, able to handle and enjoy simple trails.

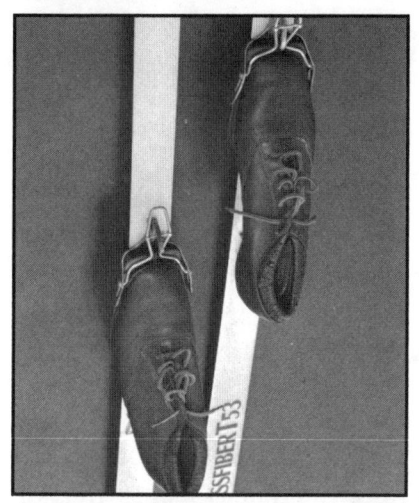

Cross coountry ski boots almost look like low cut walking shoes. They are light and flexible so the heel can rise with the skiing motion. The binding, right, is uncomplicated and just holds the toe of the boot to the binding foot plate.

Much of the technique in basic cross country skiing is similar to brisk walking. The major difference is that it is a gliding, rather than a stepping, movement. The arms swing normally, as in walking, pushing on each ski pole alternately, to assist the forward motion.

You will find your cross country shoes comfortable and flexible. They fasten to the skis at the toe, allowing the heel to rise naturally during the glide. In the beginning, however, there is a tendency to use the ski poles for balance rather than for the pushing action that needs to be combined with the sliding movement of the forward ski.

The first day, surely, will see you gliding along and beginning to feel the rhythm. It also will see you learning to get up from a fall, which is equally important to practice. While it is not too difficult to learn by oneself, instruction from a knowledgeable skier is very valuable in the initial stages. This can best be accomplished through professional instruction in a regular cross country skiing class.

For a while, you should remain on flat terrain, just sliding along practicing the glide and arm/pole coordination. It won't take long. All of a sudden, you will combine the leg and arm/pole motions for connective strides. Your speed seems to pick up without effort; rhythm smooths. You're on your way in a great sport! Further practice will rapidly build confidence and you soon will be ready to learn uphill techniques, to control your skis in different snow conditions, and how to handle more difficult terrain where the famed "telemark" turn becomes an essential technique.

SEASONAL LIMITATIONS

For most of us, skiing is a winter and early spring sport. In the U.S., the Rockies generally have the longest season with good conditions by early December and lasting through the end of March. The Rockies' season often continues even through April and part of May for those skiers willing to climb high.

There is also summer glacier skiing for those who don't get enough in winter. The Swiss Alps offer the widest choice for this category of skier. And for those who still are not satiated, then Portillo, Chile, is your spot. July and August are Chile's winter!

Which Sports For You?

TIME EXPENDED

The wonderful thing about a ski resort is that you are right there, with accommodations frequently only a few minutes from the slopes, which open around 9 a.m. and close at 4 p.m. Ski school schedules usually run two and a half hours in the morning and two and half hours in the afternoon with an hour break for lunch.

Ski classes are divided into groups that ski at the same level making the experience fun and congenial.

Don't worry. You won't be skiing all that time. Listening to your instructor's critiques and explanations, watching him or her demonstrate techniques and then waiting for your turn to practice, will use up a fair portion of the available hours. Nor do you have to ski both morning and afternoon classes. Some individuals prefer to ski one or the other. Some like skiing all day for two days and then resting the third. The die-hards will ski all day every day! In any case, ski resorts make it easy for you to schedule instructions, so your skiing time is up to you.

The cross country skier seldom needs more than one or two days in class instruction and then can proceed independently, although novice cross country skiers should stay on well marked trails. These will be nearby at most resorts.

Travel time, of course, also has to be taken into consideration. Depending upon where your home is located, snow may be near or far away. As a rule, though, the cross country skier doesn't have to travel as far as the alpine skier to find acceptable snow conditions.

INITIAL AND RECURRING COSTS

Alpine skiing is an expensive sport. Not only is skiable terrain mostly limited to ski resorts where $100 per person per day is the average cost to cover accommodations, food and ski lift tickets, but the equipment is also costly. Skis, boots, bindings and poles will total $250 to $500 plus. Finally, ski apparel, while good looking and very functional, also is very expensive. Men can get away with perhaps $200 for jacket and pants. Women's fashions can quickly run more than $500 (but who can resist those wonderful looking outfits?).

The cross country skier can ski in almost anything that is comfortable and his skis, boots, bindings and poles can be bought for $125. Although there are very attractive and fairly expensive clothes for the cross country skier, too, he or she doesn't need the wind-resistant and warmth-retaining clothes so vital for comfortable alpine skiing. Cross country skiing generates a lot of body heat and generally takes place in more protected areas. The alpine skier, on the other hand, faces the significantly greater chill factors of higher altitude, wind-swept slopes and greater speeds.

The cross country skier often can enjoy this sport with just four or five inches of snow. Thus, for those not living in the south, southeast and southwest, cross country skiing during the winter months sometimes can be out the back door or just a few hours away by car. Alpine ski resorts, however, are mostly limited to New England, the Rockies and West Coast Sierras, so travel expense has to be added to the cost of alpine skiing for most of us.

REGIONAL AVAILABILITY

Alas, the poor alpine skier who must always go where the snow is! The Friday evening exodus and return Sunday evening by

Which Sports For You?

car to Vermont from New York, to numerous resorts in the Rockies from Denver, and to Mammoth from southern California, is a fact of life from January to March. And on Saturdays during these same months, airports around the country are jammed with six-day-package skiers enroute to or returning from their favorite alpine heaven.

The cross country skier, of course, listens to the same siren song, but has wider regional choices from which to choose. Needing neither mountains nor as much snow, the cross country skier simply has a larger "snow belt" to enjoy.

FITNESS LEVEL

From the standpoint of overall fitness, alpine skiing is not so demanding aerobically. After all, you basically are just sliding down a hill. But certain fitness aspects of this sport need attention. The high altitudes (4,000 to 12,000) feet at modern ski resorts) can place considerable demand on the pulmonary and cardiovascular systems. Even at 6,000 feet, an arriving skier will experience some shortness of breath, and it usually takes a full day to acclimatize to the altitude. Restricting alcohol intake is also advisable.

It is wise to make the first run of the day a smooth warm-up on a relatively easy trail.

In addition, there is the cold. Yes, the right warmth-protecting clothes make a big difference here. The beginning skier, who cannot and should not try to ski as vigorously as the advanced skier, especially needs proper inner garments that will retain body heat on those cold days. Muscles, ligaments and limbs numbed by the cold simply do not function well and will be more prone to injury.

The arm and leg action in cross country skiing is smooth and flowing.

The ankles, knees and legs clearly bear the brunt of alpine skiing, so no one should be on the slopes who has not previously conditioned this part of the musculo-skeletal system. In addition, warm-up and stretching exercises before the day's skiing commences are strongly recommended. The first run should be on an easy slope or trail to further warm up your body. This is especially important if the morning's first lift ride up the mountain is a long one and it is a cold day.

Cross country skiing, on the other hand, is an excellent conditioning sport by itself. Only swimming may surpass it in this respect. The entire body and cardiovascular system is involved in this

Which Sports For You?

type of skiing. All the muscles, ligaments and joints from finger tips to toes are used to achieve the rhythmic gliding motion. In commencing this sport, you can ski at a slow pace with little physical or aerobic demand and then build up gradually to the intensive conditioning of a more powerful thrust and skiing rhythm.

While the usual warm–up and stretching exercises apply to cross country skiing as well, this type of skiing has two other conditioning advantages over alpine skiing. First, instead of riding a lift up the mountain and then immediately commencing downhill skiing action, the cross country skier can start walking slowly on his skis, warming up muscles and then working easily into more intensive exercises. Second, the very nature of cross country skiing's leg and arm action is smooth, usually with few of the sudden muscle and joint stresses that can occur in alpine skiing.

SKILL LEVEL FOR ENJOYMENT

Both alpine and cross country skiing reward their participants with a high degree of enjoyment even at the beginning level of skill.

The skier is moving swiftly, but in full control as she starts her turn.

SPORTS AFTER 50

Although you may start out your instruction with some trepidation about alpine skiing, you will be surprised at how quickly you can learn the fundamentals and enjoy your progress.

You will be making easy stem turns the first or second day of instruction. With that skill comes the sense of control that encourages you to let the skis run a bit and to enjoy the feeling of the skis against the snow. Today's teaching methods emphasize such confidence-building steps. The result: you start skiing more quickly and keep learning the more advanced techniques while enjoying the exhilaration inherent in this sport. As your skills develop, you will find that more difficult downhill trails and different snow conditions will always present new challenges. This is where further profes-

Following your instructor and imitating his technique is a great way to improve your skiing.

sional instruction in more advanced techniques can be so valuable. It opens the door for safer and increasingly enjoyable skiing.

The cross country skier, unlike the alpine beginner, confronts few psychological obstacles. If you can walk, you can ski. You, therefore, start out skiing immediately. If it takes time and practice to develop the smooth rhythm and speed of the advanced cross country skier, the pleasure of the skiing motion is yours right from the start. As your body warms and responds to the coordinated rhythm of arms and legs, you can be gliding through a wooded trail or along a snow-packed meadow, tasting the crisp air of a sunny winter day or, perhaps, the soft flakes of an ending snowstorm. Learning to turn on cross country skis (the telemark) is an advanced maneuver worth learning. Once mastered, you can ski safely in the hills as well as on the flat.

For both alpine and cross country skiers, it is indeed a very special world, one that can make you, too, look forward to winter.

AEROBIC QUALITIES

Cross country skiing is an excellent conditioning sport that can be used for efficient aerobic training. Not so with alpine skiing. The

And if you want a little more challenge, almost every alpine skiing resort schedules Nastar races one day a week. Racing against the clock allows you to measure your skiing level.

SPORTS AFTER 50

novice must seek such conditioning elsewhere. A long downhill run of sufficient difficulty will generate good aerobics for the more advanced skier, but seldom for more than five minutes of sustained action before another 10 to 15 minute life ride back up the mountain.

INJURY POTENTIAL

The injury potential for the alpine skier is clearly a factor to be considered. While modern equipment and teaching methods have made alpine skiing a safe sport, the relatively few injuries that occur can be severe, primarily because of the higher speeds. Skiers run into other skiers or into some object off the trail or, after a fall, the bindings don't release and the momentum of the body twisting one way while the skis twist another, can cause muscle, ligament and

The modern binding provides an easy step-in procedure and the boot is locked firmly in place.

Which Sports For You?

joint damage, or a bone fracture.

Accordingly, good ski bindings are perhaps the most important single piece of equipment. Bindings are designed to release when pressure against them is too severe for that person's skiing ability, conditioning and technique. Proper bindings, therefore, have multiple settings to reflect different levels of release. It is critical that these be set correctly. For the beginning skier, and also for someone less athletic or less well conditioned, this means placing the setting at the point of easiest release that is proper for that person's weight.

Setting the binding correctly is particularly important when renting equipment. Most ski resorts insist that rental shops be staffed with qualified technicians. Injuries do not help the resort. Some individuals, perhaps embarrassed to say they are beginners, will intimate they ski at the intermediate level. Don't do this! The binding release point will then be set at a too advanced position for you. Always check out the release action immediately when renting skis. If the bindings don't release well in the shop, they won't on the slopes either.

Ski resort trails are well groomed and also are clearly marked for the level of ability the user is expected to have. Skiing on a trail marked above your true ability level is asking for trouble. You will find that injuries seldom occur in a ski school class. This is not because they are skiing slowly, but because the instructor selects trails and snow conditions that fit the level of the students in that class.

Boots and skis also play a role. Poorly fitting boots not only lead to great discomfort, but also to bad skiing techniques that can make a fall more likely. Take time to buy or rent boots that fit well. Similarly, skis that are too long or too stiff for your level of skill also can be dangerous. Your instructor will quickly assess your skill. Listen to his recommendations and follow them.

The above advice will minimize the dangers of an injury, but remember that alpine skiing is not a conditioning sport by itself. The skiing action of turning, stopping, absorbing the terrain bumps all can apply stress on ankles, knees and legs. Ski only if these body parts are reasonably well conditioned. It is not difficult to achieve this. Walking or bicycling plus the leg exercises recommended in

SPORTS AFTER 50

Chapter III and Chapter VII are excellent activities to ready yourself for alpine skiing on well-groomed trails.

Cross country skiing has a minimum potential for injury, even at the intermediate skiing level. One generally is skiing along rather flat terrain or through wooded trails that are free of obstacles. If you choose to make your own trail in deeper snow, however, look out for hidden obstacles.

As you learn advanced techniques like the telemark and challenge deeper and heavier snow conditions in hilly or mountainous areas, you also must become knowledgeable about the terrain and weather. In such areas, you should initially ski with a guide and, in any case, never ski alone. The risk is not a crippling fall, but possibly being unable to extricate yourself if a ski gets caught at a bad angle in very deep snow, or perhaps breaks. A relatively short distance to hike on skis can become a nightmarish struggle on foot in deep snow.

Demonstrating the telemark turn.

Which Sports For You?

A mixture of flat and rolling terrain is ideal for cross country skiing.

The cross country boot and binding attachment allow the foot, ankle and leg to twist without undue strain, so there is little danger of a serious sprain or more serious damage from a fall. On the other hand, there is some loss of stability because the binding is flexible and the ski is long and narrow. As a result, balance at first seems unsteady. Although some falls are commonplace at this beginning stage, these are not apt to cause injury.

Since cross country skiing offers such excellent conditioning opportunities, it is a particularly fine sport for generating productive fitness. Endurance and strength can be built gradually without imposing excessive strain on any section of the body. Because the poling action does call on the less used arm, shoulder and back muscles, however, exercises to develop flexibility and strength in those areas are advisable.

CAN YOU DO IT ALONE?

No question about it; both alpine and cross country skiing are sports for the individual. Yet they are wonderful family sports, a fact that has helped to make the ski resort industry successful. You should only ski alone on well marked alpine trails that are guarded by ski patrols.

SOCIABILITY

Both of these skiing activities seem to generate a large degree of sociability. Partly it is the weather and time of year. For too many Americans 50-and-over, winter is only a cold, unpleasant period during which living is largely indoors. Snow becomes just a miserable hazard. For the skier, it is just the opposite. Snow brings a wonderful sport. This joy rubs off on others and there is a certain joyousness on the slopes and trails that is matched by few other endeavors.

Also, there is the sense of well being that is stimulated by a day of outdoor winter exercise. If a day's skiing, followed by a Jacuzzi or hot tub, a pleasant drink and a good dinner doesn't strip you of mundane worries, something is indeed wrong. Be honest; have you ever heard of a skier who takes along sleeping pills?

A New England inn hosts a group of cross country skiers.

SWIMMING AND SNORKELING

When you were taught to swim those many years ago, your family probably had two main thoughts: first was the safety factor of your knowing how to swim; next, swimming is a healthy summer time activity almost every kid will enjoy.

If you are no longer an enthusiastic swimmer (60 to 70 degree water can feel a lot colder now than when you were younger, while chlorine in pools often is hard on the eyes), the modern wetsuit and goggles can make swimming truly pleasurable again.

Wetsuit Swimming

Yes, the same stretchy neoprene wetsuits that boardsailors wear to keep warm on those cool, windy days, also make a nifty protective layer for the swimmer. Fitting like an outer skin, wetsuits come in three styles to cover only as much of the body as you wish. There is the "longjohn" that covers the legs as well as upper body; the "shortie" for the upper body and hips only; and a simple vest for the upper body alone. For maximum warmth, a longjohn covering the arms can be worn as well. The wetsuit allows full freedom of motion while retaining your body heat. Try one using two-millimeter neoprene thickness for 60 to 75 degree water and three millimeters if colder.

Snorkeling

Don't confuse the kids' old toy outfits with modern snorkeling equipment. Today's sophisticated masks are fog-free, shaped and sized to fit differing facial structures, and they allow the snorkel (breathing tube) to adjust securely and comfortably. There also are various type fins to match foot size and intended use, so put on your wetsuit and snorkeling gear and venture out into the water.

Try a shallow, but swimmable depth and have someone show you how to expel water through the snorkel. Float around with your head under water but with the snorkel sticking above and practice breathing. Then take a deep breath, hold it, and dive below the surface. In both cases, you will be surprised at how easily the fins propel you and how interesting the underwater scene becomes now that you can actually see it. You may get a few unexpected mouthfuls of water the first few times you try snorkeling, but we predict you soon will be reading those resort brochures that offer, "Exciting snorkeling in beautiful lagoons!"

The Non-Swimmer

If you can't swim or have never learned to swim well enough to feel comfortable and safe in the water, why not learn now?

Buoyancy: Did you know that older persons often are more buoyant than the young? You may find that at your present age, you tend to float easily and can sustain a comfortable breathing rhythm using a simple and natural stroke. You also will find that many communities now offer swimming programs tailored to adult beginners.

The simple side stroke facilitates breathing

Safety: Look at it this way — maybe you will never choose to do a lot of swimming, but why be paralyzed by fear at the thought? Also, if you can swim, you may save someone else's life too.

Which Sports For You?

Fun Sports: Swimming safely not only can introduce you to snorkeling, but also opens up those other fun sports on the water such as boardsailing, canoeing, rowing and small boat sailing. You don't have to become a polished swimmer, just a safe one.

Health: Swimming not only ranks with rowing and cross country skiing as one of the best overall body conditioning activities, but is especially suitable for individuals with arthritis, muscular or other joint motion problems. The water's density supports much of the body's weight, and, arm and leg motion becomes more comfortable. "Water aerobics" is an enjoyable group activity as well as valuable exercise for those with restricted joint movement.

EASE OF LEARNING

Modern techniques have revolutionized the teaching of swimming, particularly in overcoming the fear of sinking and its corollary, the fear of not being able to breathe or get enough air. These are the two main obstacles for the non-swimmer. The actual swimming strokes are natural arm and leg motions that can be learned almost instinctively.

A good swimming instruction program moves you step by step away from your fears.

Water aerobics continues to grow in popularity.

Practicing in shallow depths, you will learn the proper breathing sequence and how buoyant the body is in the water. Soon you will be swimming short distances, developing your confidence and finding a rhythm that suits you.

There are four basic and widely recognized strokes: the crawl, breast stroke; back stroke; and side stroke. You probably will find one of these easiest to learn. Starting with that one, you will quickly overcome any lingering fears. Try the other strokes, too. You may not feel as comfortable at first, but they are all easy to learn. You will find that each uses different arm and leg motions. This allows you to rest one set of muscles when you shift strokes and provides a valuable change of pace.

It won't be long until you also experiment with swimming underwater. Once you have done this a few times, you will recognize its pleasurable, almost sensual feeling. It also will eliminate one of those old fears, for you will find that the water tries to push you to the surface, not pull you down.

SEASONAL LIMITATIONS

Weather is not a serious problem with the exception of swimming outside during an electrical storm. Swimmers generally can arrange indoor swimming during cool months. Water temperature outdoors, however, is always a factor and even when the water seemingly is warm, the air often is chilly. Thus a wetsuit can become a practical accessory, if not a necessity. Snorkelers, however, will wear wetsuits much of the time. Water temperature may be quite warm on the surface, but it drops rapidly as one descends. Also, the snorkeler normally doesn't exercise as intensively as the swimmer, so generates less body heat.

COSTS

Most of the time the expense is minimal, though an indoor swimming program can easily run $15 to $20 per week. The neoprene wetsuits will cost around $100 for the longjohn; $50 for the shorty; and $25-$35 for the vest. Suitable snorkeling gear for the beginner can be purchased for $50 or less. Of course, it could be several hundred dollars more after adding round trip air fare to the Caribbean and its enticing snorkeling lagoons, but you were going to visit there anyway, weren't you?

TIME EXPENDED

Swimming 20-30 minutes at a steady but moderate pace exercises the body fully, plus provides significant aerobic conditioning, so this sport is particularly attractive to those who seek a good workout within a minimum time.

Snorkeling, on the other hand, is a slower paced activity in which cruising through and around the underwater scenery is some-

Which Sports For You?

thing to be leisurely enjoyed.

REGIONAL AVAILABILITY

Given the number of private clubs, individual and community pools along with the thousands of lakes and miles of ocean shore, there is clearly no dearth of swimming opportunities. Water pollution problems have been steadily encroaching upon an increasing number of lakes and rivers, but rising community concern may yet reverse this trend, so, "Bring your bathing suit," is still basic advice for visiting almost any region in our country.

FITNESS LEVEL

No other sport can surpass swimming's benefits for every level of fitness. Whether attempting major health rehabilitation, initiating a moderate conditioning program or entering intensive physical training, one can find significant advantages in a swimming program.

For example, a person standing in water up to the neck experiences a functioning weight loss of about 90 per cent. This allows individuals with painful joints or severely weakened muscles to move their extremities more comfortably. Such action and exercise can then promote the flexibility, strength and muscle endurance otherwise prevented either by the excessive discomfort of usual movement or by the action limits of severely debilitated muscles.

On the other hand, by carefully monitoring the pace and distance of swimming workouts, an individual commencing a new fitness program — or intensifying an existing one — can reach and maintain almost any desired fitness level.

SKILL LEVEL FOR ENJOYMENT

Another great advantage for swimming is the minimum skill level necessary for enjoyment. Once you have learned how to breathe while in the water, and to use the simple arm and leg motions which best propel the body, all you have to do is just swim. Even the beginner will enjoy swimming and can rapidly learn the strokes and breathing sequence that bring full confidence in the water. One can become a strong swimmer without necessarily becoming a polished swimmer.

Once you are swimming confidently in flat water, you are ready for small waves or choppy water. When you become fully at ease in those conditions, you then are ready to tackle surf. Body surfing in waves is tremendously exhilarating. You need to be a strong swimmer, though, and to know a lot about the particular beach, wave motion and undertow conditions to body surf safely.

AEROBIC QUALITIES

Since swimming involves sustained use of much of the body's muscular system, its aerobic effects are great. This makes swimming an excellent companion activity for other sports that do not provide as much aerobic conditioning.

INJURY POTENTIAL

While there is almost no injury potential in the swimming motion itself, bad judgment accidents continue to occur. Most of these are youth-oriented such as diving into water that is too shallow, swimming at night or during an electrical storm. But there are two less obvious hazards worth noting. The first, which is very risky, is swimming farther or faster than one's conditioning warrants. The relaxing quality of more leisurely swimming can be dangerously offset by the sudden increase in heart rate generated by intensive swimming. Every swimmer should know the maximum swimming pace that can be maintained and for how long, while keeping the heart rate within acceptable limits for age and condition.

The second is less serious, but also important to monitor and this is water quality. Assuming that it does meet regular pollution standards, infections of eyes, ears and sinus can still occur, especially for those who are sensitive in any of these areas. Goggles and ear plug may help, but individuals with existing problems should only swim with their doctor's approval.

CAN IT BE ENJOYED ALONE?

This point hardly needs mentioning except, perhaps, in reverse. Pool swimming generally has other persons in the immediate area and also has a close-by shallow end should a debilitating cramp or other serious pain occur. For lake, river or ocean swimming, however, make a practice of swimming with someone else. It can be companionable and, most important, it is a *safety* precaution.

SOCIABILITY

Floating or paddling lazily in a pool while conversing with others can, indeed, be enjoyable, but it is hardly swimming. Doing pool laps or swimming in a large body of water requires a concentrated muscular effort and a correct breathing sequence, so conversation with others is impossible. As with a growing number of senior sports activities, however, swimming offers national, regional and local competition for different age classifications and levels of ability.

There always has been warm camaraderie among swimmers and whether you are just starting a program — or returning to the active swimmer you once were — you will find easy companionship in this fine sport.

SPORTS AFTER 50

SMALL BOAT SAILING

With canoeing, boardsailing, swimming and rowing, why include another water sport such as small boat sailing? There are some excellent reasons.

First, it is one of the oldest established sports — one that, traditionally, has attracted individuals of all ages and can offer a particularly wide range of activity to those 50-and-over. The same thing can perhaps be said for large cruising sailboats in terms of being enjoyable for all ages, but the latter do not provide the kinds of physical exercise and intense, individual action that is so much a part of small boat sailing and racing. Nor, of course, are the large boats affordable or practical for most.

The great annual "river race" for the Sunfish Class.

Which Sports For You?

Don't let anyone kid you. Small boat sailing and racing are not in the least sedentary, although sitting down is the basic position! Whether you are racing one of the single-handed boats like a Sunfish, Laser or small catamaran, or two-person boats like the Finn, Jet 14 or larger catamarans, the experience can be a full workout of bending, pulling, balancing and sliding quickly from side to side, or, on the contrary, having to endure a cramped position so as not to disturb the boat's balance and speed in a light wind race. In high winds or in a sudden whipping squall, the energy, quick movements and body coordination needed just to keep the boat upright, let alone stay on course at maximum speed, can test anyone's athletic and competitive abilities.

Also, small boat sailing need not be at all competitive. True, every sailor becomes a bit compulsive about getting his boat to sail as fast as it can, but the one-design classes all have set dimensions and equipment specifications. Thus, a sailor can't improve his boat's performance through some special equipment advantage, but only through his or her own skill. And this provides a perpetual challenge. Small adjustments in the rigging, mast angle, set of the sails and balance of the boat are just some of the areas that sailors will test and alter, seeking maximum performance and not necessarily just to win races. There is a special satisfaction all in itself in fine tuning a boat.

Of course, you can enjoy casual sailing, too. The love affair between owner and sailboat probably goes back to the Sumerians of the 4th millenium B.C. — the earliest sailors history records. It surely has not diminished today. Insult someone's boat only at your peril!

While not all small sailboats are racing design classes, the majority are, so most such sailors easily can compare their performances. If fine tuning the boat is a constant compulsion, fine tuning the skipper and crew is an endless search for perfection. Sailors are never content with their knowledge, and rightfully so. Seldom, if ever, are the wind, waves and currents precisely the same. And thus, sailors all over the world will continue to share unique experiences with each other in their constant search for more knowledge.

No, you won't get bored when you learn to sail. The endless dimensions and facets of sailing become yours for life. The range of satisfaction constantly grows. Try small boat sailing; you won't go wrong.

EASE OF LEARNING

Learning to sail is not difficult, just time consuming. The basic skills can be acquired after a few hours of instruction. Learning to apply those skills correctly in shifting winds, when unusual tide or currents are present, or when visibility is limited, requires knowledge and techniques that take time to absorb.

Sailing is not a sport to initiate by oneself — the price for error is too high. Competent sailing schools exist along our country's coastline and in numerous inland waterway locations or at large lakes. This is a good investment for every beginner. Any experienced sailor, however, can teach you the basic skills in protected waters, using a two-person boat of the Sunfish type, or any other small boat with the jib lowered.

You will first learn how and why a boat moves under sail, the different courses it can sail in relation to the wind direction, as well

A sailing school always includes land instruction and explanation before getting underway.

Which Sports For You?

as those courses it cannot sail such as directly into the wind or, generally, on any course up to a 45-degree angle on either side of the direction from which the wind is blowing. Boat and sail handling come next and will be readily absorbed if the techniques are first demonstrated to the beginner, then practiced while the instructor critiques.

Possibly the most confusing aspect for the neophyte is the sailor's language. Is all that nautical terminology necessary? Definitely not in learning basic sailing skills in a small boat. You will quickly pick up the few essential words and phrases such as bow, stern, port, starboard, windward, leeward and sheet, etc. Additional terminology will logically fit into your sailing vocabulary when and as there is a practical need. Such intricacies as the parts of the boat can all be learned from the many excellent books about sailing or from advanced sailing courses.

So, put confusing terminology aside and go for the feel of sailing. Feel the way a boat steers, responds to the pressure of the wind against the sail, and changes speed depending on its course in relation to the wind. You will quickly learn that you can control the boat's speed, stability and proper course — and this feeling is the essence of sailing! At this point, you can benefit greatly from those books about sailboat handling and it becomes worthwhile to struggle with that nautical terminology.

TIME EXPENDED

Sailing can be time consuming not just because there's a lot to learn, but also because the sport becomes so absorbing. Put two sailors together and the uninitiated will never get in a word.

On the other hand, a pleasant sail is not necessarily time consuming at all. Small boats are easily trailerable and can be rigged and launched quickly at any marina. A few free hours is all you need for a relaxing sail, or bring along a picnic lunch and make it a delightful day.

SEASONAL LIMITATIONS

Anyone who has heard of the Frostbite Series knows this refers to winter racing in small sailboats. Their motto is: "If it isn't frozen completely, it's sailable." If the frostbiters remain a fairly small group of sailors, that word nevertheless describes the wide weather range for this sport. No wind at all or gales are other limiting factors. Neither of these are that frequent. With good judgment, along with knowledge of local weather patterns, plus the right clothes, sailors can spend much of the year on the water.

INITIAL AND RECURRING COSTS

The Sunfish is perhaps the least expensive and most successful one-design class ever produced. While it will cost close to $2,000 fully rigged for a new one, its strong fiberglass construction and aluminum mast give the Sunfish a long life. The Laser and other one-design classes are more expensive, primarily because expense increases as the design and rigging options become more sophisticated. The smaller catamarans, on the other hand, are close to the Sunfish in price.

All these boats have a ready second-hand market. If the boat is in good condition, expect to pay roughly two-thirds to half of the original price. A good used boat will sail very well and can be sub-

Its economy and ease of launching make the Sunfish a good schooling boat for beginners.

Which Sports For You?

sequently sold and return much of its cost. The other initial investment is a small trailer, which can cost $200 to over $1,000.

Sails can get torn or "blown out". Repairing a torn sail is not expensive. New ones cost $300 and up. If you store your boat at a marina, there will be that monthly charge. Otherwise, launching fees at most public marinas run between $2 and $5.

Basically, then, the recurring expenses for small sailboats are not much. This, along with the minimum maintenance work resulting from good fiberglass construction, makes your continuing investment one of pleasure, not money.

REGIONAL AVAILABILITY

Trailerability is one of the small sailboat's many advantages along with its minimal draft, a requirement for sailing in shallow water. Lakes and inland waterways are its habitat, although boats like the Sunfish and catamarans can be easily launched from a beach when the surf is mild.

Every one-design sailor knows those regions of the country in which fleets of that particular class are raced. Monthly sailing magazines and regional journals publish regatta schedules for all one-

Small boats are easily stored on shore.

design classes. As a result, there is a constant interchange of information that helps strengthen the one-design concept and expand interest around the country.

Most resorts at the shore also will have Sunfish and catamarans for rent and some will have sailing classes. This is particularly true for the Caribbean resorts. The more sophisticated one-design class boats seldom will be available for rent, since they require special knowledge and skill to sail and could be too easily damaged.

FITNESS LEVEL

This is difficult to quantify. If you choose to sail casually and only in light winds, you will never need conditioning beyond the general fitness which allows easy movement and proper balance in a small boat. If you enjoy venturing into stronger winds, then your shoulders, back, arms and wrists will surely be exercised. Catamarans and other high performance boats demand increasing levels of agility and conditioning. If you become interested in racing — and active senior classifications exist in several one-design classes — you will find yourself exercising most of your body (and if you're a perfectionist, you also can clean and polish your boat endlessly). Somehow, most small boat owners remain fit. There must be a good reason.

SKILL LEVEL FOR ENJOYMENT

All forms of sailing demand the same basic knowledge of wind forces and how these power the sail and also affect, if not determine, the course you can steer. Each sailboat type has its own stability limits too, so this factor plus the boat's rigging and steering characteristics are all part of the fundamentals a person must absorb.

Yet, the pleasure commences as you first start to practice those techniques that control the boat's speed, course and safety.

The first time you steer a sailboat you will feel the delicate qualities of sailing and also sense the tremendous strength of the wind and water's combined forces. Thus, along with the great pleasure of learning to sail, there is a growing recognition (and awe) of those two powerful elements with which you must learn to cope. Good

Which Sports For You?

sailors enjoy pushing their boats to the limit, but they never forget that the real limit is set by the wind and water, not their own skill. Small sailboats are vulnerable to squalls and storms. Safely riding out extreme weather conditions often can be accomplished by knowledgeable sailors. Avoiding them is always wiser.

AEROBIC QUALITIES

The small boat sailor will get a lot of good exercise, but no aerobic training.

CAN YOU DO IT ALONE?

Yes, and this quality makes the small sailboat particularly attractive to many. Almost any small sailboat, however, is built to hold two persons, even though it usually may be sailed or raced by just one person. Some hold three or more. Never, however, load a boat beyond its rated capacity.

INJURY POTENTIAL

Other than errors in judgment, which generally relate to unfamiliarity with sailing's *Rules of the Road,* sailing in dangerous weather, unknown waters, or attempting maneuvers that are beyond one's skill, sailing produces few injuries. But accidents can happen. There are two cardinal safety rules: 1. A U.S. Coast Guard-approved life jacket for each crew member or passenger should always be on board. It always should be worn in rough conditions and it is wise to wear one at all times regardless of weather; 2. If capsized or swamped, stay with the boat. Never try to swim for shore no matter how strong a swimmer you may be. Your sailboat should have built-in flotation and always check to make sure before you rent or buy one. This keeps the boat from sinking if swamped or capsized. You and the boat are much more visible than a lonely swimmer. More critical, currents, waves and water temperature can easily prevent the swimmer from reaching shore.

SOCIABILITY

Small boat sailors seem to recognize each other wherever they are.

Less formal than the large sailboat racing fraternity, the competitive rivalry in the various one-design classes is no less keen. Men and women sail against each other with no quarter asked, but this sport seems to generate an especially friendly bond among participants. New sailors always will be helped, but not coddled. "Paying your dues," has come to mean not the expense of a club's fee, but the embarrassment of making those sailing mistakes that every sailor must experience as the price of developing the necessary knowledge and skill.

HIKING

We are all walkers of some kind, so the sport of hiking is a natural activity for anyone. Millions already enjoy it; millions more should sample its rewards!

As with biking, many communities offer their own hiking club. Regional hiking associations abound throughout the country and the National Parks system offers miles of splendid trails, some of which have support facilities such as overnight cabins. Although the city, with its dense traffic and crowded streets is not the most desirable place for hikers, even urban dwellers still find enjoyment walking in the early morning hours when auto traffic is minimal and the air is fresh.

Admittedly, though, when we picture hiking, the image is a more rural environment, one with rolling hills or even more rugged terrain. Not surprisingly, when walking no longer had to be our basic transportation, hiking for pleasure commenced to grow as a sport. And its popularity is truly well deserved. What other sport is so totally natural in concept, can be engaged in no matter where one lives, can be enjoyed in any season, is free and needs no specialized instruction? And, of course, walking lends itself perfectly to almost any conditioning program.

On one hand, a modest daily walking program is one exercise always recommended for those recovering from surgery, heart attack or other serious illness. At the other extreme, speed walking and/or intensive hiking under backpack conditions can test anyone's aerobic conditioning and fitness. There are, in fact, few limits or barriers to this wonderful activity. Enjoyable alone and companionable with others, it offers pleasures to fit almost any style. Even those who seek a competitive incentive can find this in the intensive action of trekking, a relatively new sport in which individuals train to achieve certain climbing and distance goals within a specific period.

Other than a good pair of walking shoes, available at any outdoor sports store, you need no special equipment or clothes. Like all sports, though, hiking also has developed its own particular type of equipment and clothing accessories. These relate primarily to comfort and safety considerations. As your hiking ventures expand, you will soon learn which of these are important and which are not.

So, don't wait any longer. Whether you become an inveterate hiker or an occasional one, you will find it rewarding both as a sport in its own right and as a supporting activity for fitness conditioning. It is something you can commence right at your own doorstep, or make into an exhilarating adventure in some other part of our country, or in a foreign land you have always wanted to visit.

Unlike the other sports described in this chapter, walking is something we all are skilled at and, unless handicapped through injury or illness, something we can do almost any time we wish. Costs, time limitations, locations, fitness, skill levels, seasonal limitations and most other characteristics need no explanation here. Perhaps the one exception comes under the heading of *Injury Potential.*

Under normal conditions, this potential is very low. Legs can be conditioned gradually through increasing the distance and speed of walking and, although ankle and knee sprains can occur, these are unlikely in flat terrain if good shoes and minimal care are used.

At the same time, hiking, as opposed to just walking, is apt to take us into terrain and circumstances with which we may not be so well acquainted. Even a day's hiking can bring us into unfamiliar territory. Overnight trips obviously involve longer distances and possible isolation from communication facilities. In either situation, one can find oneself some distance from assistance should that be needed.

For this reason, hiking alone, though enjoyable, is clearly less safe than with a companion who can provide assistance (or can obtain it) if an incapacitating accident occurs. If you feel more comfortable with a walking stick, take one. As you move on to hiking unfamiliar places, a strong and well balanced hiking stick can be useful

Which Sports For You?

in various ways. Beyond providing balance over rough terrain or testing soft and unsure ground, it facilitates a "standing rest". It also can prop up your back pack into a needed back support when you are seated while in open country.

Finally, if you decide to explore the joys of hiking, invest in that outstanding informational resource, *The Complete Walker*, by Colin Fletcher. First published in 1968, it has been reprinted six times and was revised in 1978. For most sports, there is no single book that provides all the information one might need. The hiking enthusiast is lucky. As the magazine *Field & Stream* has noted, Fletcher's book is truly, "The hiker's bible". It is impossible to imagine any consideration about hiking that is not well covered by this superb book.

OUTDOOR SPORTS AND HYPOTHERMIA

Although the question of injury potential has been reviewed for each of the sports discussed in this chapter, there is one safety consideration that can affect all outdoor sports activity and that is hypothermia. Everyone should know about its danger and how it should be avoided.

Hypothermia occurs whenever the body temperature drops below normal and reaches a point at which the body loses the capacity to re-warm itself. If corrective steps are not taken immediately, this condition escalates. In more advanced stages, only medical assistance can help a hypothermia victim to survive, and even the best professional knowledge often is not successful.

Since hypothermia is so dangerous, yet also can be avoided by a few basic and simple precautions, why does it continue to happen? The answer is two-fold. First, nearly everyone assumes, because the danger results from sub-normal body temperature, that hypothermia is only a winter, or cold climate problem. Ironically, most occurrences take place in spring, summer and fall months. Second, individuals tend to assume they will not be outside in bad weather unless properly clothed. Unfortunately, it is beautiful weather which suddenly turns bad that generally creates situations leading to danger of hypothermia.

If you know the weather circumstances that can precipitate the danger and understand why those conditions can occur in any season, you will never ignore the possibility that it can happen. This means that the extra set of dry clothing, suitable protective gear and also some quick energy food will always be on hand to guard against hypothermia when enjoying outdoor sports.

Remember that each of the following four factors influences heat loss. Their combined presence can quickly lower body temperature to the danger point.

Fatigue: We tend to think that fatigue occurs primarily from over-exertion. It can also result from illness, lack of sleep or insufficient food. Its presence inevitably reduces one's energy level and energy is critical to the body's heat-making ability.

Wetness: Dry clothing protects body heat by trapping warm air between the clothing and your skin. When clothing becomes wet, the warm air is not only immediately lost, but the wetness -- even from clothes that are only damp -- conducts heat away from the body extremely swiftly.

Wind: Too often wind chill is associated just with winter weather and strong winds. Actually, the chilling process commences with the slightest movement of air. Only 2 mph of wind velocity provides almost two thirds of the maximum chilling effect purely from the wind. Also, the chilling action by wind takes place at any temperature. Air temperature of 58 degrees Farenheit with a 2 mph wind velocity, for example, becomes the equivalent in body comfort to an air temperature of only 30 degrees with no wind.

Air Temperature: The faster and lower the outside air temperature drops obviously affects body temperature. This in turn also heightens the impact of the above three factors on your body.

Under normal conditions, the body, when cold, shivers to generate heat. This action, along with the body warmth that can be produced by exercising and/or adding another layer of dry, windbreaking clothing usually will suffice to quickly return the body to a safe and comfortable temperature. Food, to restore energy loss, can also play an important role at this point.

If, however, you are caught without shelter in a sudden storm with its rain, wind and customary drop in air temperature, the equation is drastically altered. Unless all wet clothes are immediately replaced with dry ones, plus adding wind-breaking protection, your body temperature can quickly drop below normal and hypothermia commences. Remaining in wet clothes too long leaves no escape in such conditions. Even quick food energy and body movement cannot generate enough heat to balance the outflow from wet clothes and chill.

Remember, too, that hypothermia is extremely dangerous even in the earliest stages because its onset greatly reduces one's mental acuity. In effect, one rapidly loses the judgment to take whatever might be the best corrective action. This unfortunate tendency, in turn, is accompanied by a growing state of lethargy that further speeds up the debilitating process. Muscles become numb, the body feels no pain -- only a deep desire to rest -- all of which causes one's energy level to further drop and the deadly cycle accelerates.

So bring along that extra clothing, food and correct "wet gear" for any outdoor sport or venture you undertake. Keep it dry and handy, and even if you never get caught by those dangerous conditions that lead to hypothermia, you may save the life of someone else who is not as prepared as you.

CHAPTER III
Getting Started

Yes, it is easy to start a fitness program, but it's a lot easier to put off starting until tomorrow, next week or, "sometime soon". This, unfortunately, is precisely how most of us have arrived at our 50-and-over age, occasionally being concerned about our fitness, but having taken no direct action toward getting in better shape.

Why wait any longer? Simply make an appointment today with your doctor for a thorough physical examination. Given the doctor's likely schedule, this will provide you two more weeks of grace anyway.

But that appointment is the first step and if you have been avoiding an annual checkup, it will serve that purpose too. Specifically, however, this examination must provide a current evaluation of your cardiovascular and pulmonary system. You need to know, to the degree possible, just how well that combined system is functioning before you start active conditioning.

For most of us — even if somewhat overweight, short on stamina and lacking good muscle tone — this critical system will be operating properly and we can immediately undertake normal fitness conditioning.

Should the examination indicate a possible cardiovascular flaw, however, this too is crucial information. In this situation, your doctor may also recommend a stress or treadmill test to further determine the accuracy and/or seriousness of that initial indication. A treadmill test measures how well your cardiovascular system performs during physical exercise and, in particular, under conditions in which your heart rate approaches the maximum allowable for your age.

In spite of the possibility of false readings from a treadmill test, most doctors believe it provides important additional information once an initial physical examination indicates an apparent flaw in the cardiovascular system.

Although some disagreement still exists within the medical profession as to the role and importance of intensive exercise in avoiding heart and cardiovascular problems, there is almost unanimous medical agreement that regular and appropriate exercise is essential to recuperation from such malfunctions. It seems logical, therefore, that a well-planned, intelligent conditioning program can, at the very least, be valuable preventive medicine for anyone, a recommendation strongly supported by the recently published Paffenbarger Study.

Again, intelligent conditioning is simply a program that realistically fits you; that is, conditioning that is realistic in terms of your age, present physical condition, general physique, and exercise patterns over previous years. In turn, this means setting objectives that are safe and obtainable. Achieving these provides the important base-line fitness level that also opens the door to fun sports. There are three aspects to this level of fitness: 1. Aerobics; 2. Upper and lower body strengthening, and, 3. Flexibility.

For authoritative writing on the broad subject of cardiovascular fitness, the role of aerobics plus testing and guidelines for intensive fitness training, we refer you to books by Kenneth H. Cooper, M.D., M.P.H. His first book, Aerobics (1968 - M. Evans and Co., Inc., New York), was instrumental in starting millions of Americans on the path to fitness.

Aerobic exercise is concerned with the endurance aspect of fit-

Getting Started

ness. Some call this stamina. It does not focus on muscle strength, but is primarily concerned with the health of the heart, the lungs and the whole cardiovascular system.

The goal of aerobics exercise is to improve our proficiency in delivering oxygen to all areas of the body where, combined with stored food, it produces energy. A poor delivery capability means limited energy capacity, which then leads to less physical activity and a cycle of further fitness deterioration.

Dr. Cooper defines aerobics as, "Exercise that stimulates heart and lung activity for a time period sufficiently long to produce beneficial changes in the body." He goes on to say, "The main objective of an aerobic exercise program is to increase the maximum amount of oxygen that the body can process within a given time. This is called your aerobic capacity and depends upon efficient lungs, a powerful heart and good vascular system."

Dr. Cooper's extensive research is persuasive not only regarding the importance of aerobic exercise, but also the value of a properly designed and monitored treadmill test for anyone over 40 who is about to initiate a serious fitness program, even though that person's physical examination indicates no evidence of a cardiovascular problem. Although the aerobic exercise you are about to start — walking, bicycling or swimming — normally won't be intensive, you nevertheless will be aiming at a training effect. This means bringing your heart rate up to at least 65 percent of the maximum approved level for your age and sustaining that level for a period of 20 minutes.

Accordingly, if you have been relatively sedentary or have not engaged in regular exercise for several years, it would be hard to argue against the value of a properly conducted stress test as a preliminary step. By indicating the way your cardiovascular system responds to physical stress, this treadmill test signals the level of exercise suitable for you.

Assuming you are cleared to commence an exercise program, you need to know two specific figures concerning your heart rate. The first is your maximum approved heart rate. It is determined by a simple formula that involves merely subtracting your age from 220. If you are 50, for example, your maximum approved heart rate becomes 170. This is a heart rate you should never surpass, even briefly.

Maximum Allowable Heart Rate By Age

Age	Maximum Pulse	Age	Maximum Pulse	Age	Maximum Pulse
50	170	60	160	70	150
51	169	61	159	71	144
52	168	62	158	72	148
53	167	63	157	73	147
54	166	64	156	74	146
55	165	65	155	75	145
56	164	66	154	76	144
57	163	67	153	77	143
58	162	68	152	78	142
59	161	69	151	79	141

The second vital number is your training heart rate. This is the pulse rate range suitable for sustained aerobic exercise, meaning the

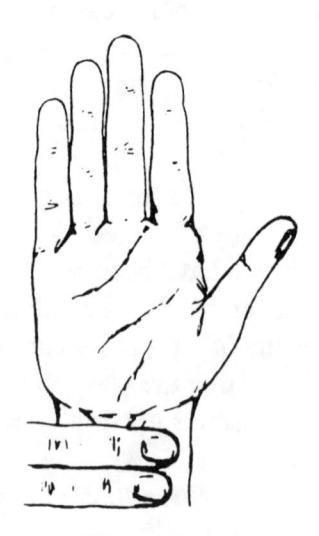

Taking pulse rate at wrist

Getting Started

exercising time necessary to achieve a training effect.

The lower end of this pulse rate range is 65 percent of your maximum allowable heart rate; the upper end is 75 percent. For instance, a 50-year-old person would have a range of 110 to 127 (figured .65 x 170 =110; and .75 x 170=127). It is generally agreed that approximately 20 minutes of sustained heart work within this range, three times per week, will satisfactorily maintain aerobic conditioning. Sustained heart work beyond this target level, however, is considered hazardous.

Target Pulse Rate Range By Age

Age	Target	Age	Target	Age	Target
50	110-127	60	104-120	70	97-112
51	110-127	61	104-119	71	97-112
52	109-126	62	103-118	72	96-111
53	109-126	63	103-118	73	96-111
54	108-125	64	101-117	74	95-110
55	107-124	65	101-116	75	94-109
56	107-123	66	100-116	76	94-108
57	106-122	67	99-115	77	93-107
58	105-121	68	99-114	78	92-107
59	105-121	69	98-113	79	92-106

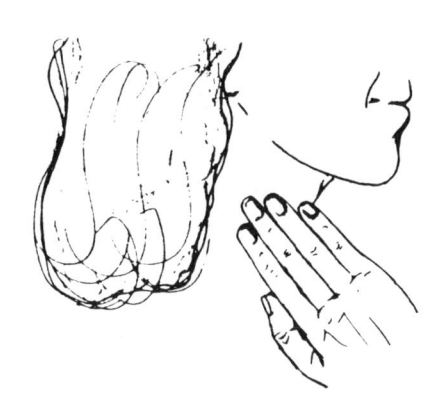

Taking pulse rate at neck

So, learning to take your own pulse rate is important. It also is quite easy. Count your pulse rate for 15 seconds and multiply by four (counting for 10 seconds and multiplying by six is less accurate). The easiest areas for taking the pulse are at the wrist on the thumb side, and at the neck right under the jaw between the wind pipe and front neck muscle where the neck and jaw line converge. The neck area often provides a clearer reading, particularly while exercising. Slide your first or middle finger from the wind pipe over to the neck muscle to find the pulse beat. Whether using the wrist or neck area, remember to press gently. Pressing too hard collapses the artery, making it impossible to feel the pulse.

STARTING YOUR PROGRAM

Choose walking, stationary cycling or swimming for your initial aerobic exercising program. Walking is the most practical for many. Indoor stationary cycling is preferred by those who have had prior leg or joint problems or who live in unpredictable climates. Swimming is considered to be a superb overall body conditioner, but it has the drawback of too easily pushing one's heart rate above the acceptable target level. Also, different swimming methods make the workout difficult to measure. Since the majority of persons can undertake either walking or stationary cycling, those are the two programs discussed here.

Unless you already are in quite good condition, it is unlikely you can reach and maintain the upper limits of your target pulse range during the early weeks without undue and possibly dangerous fatigue, regardless of which exercise you select. Fatigue is to be avoided. The idea is to work toward your full target range in easy and safe increments. Thus during the initial weeks, you will be walking a shorter distance at a slower pace. If cycling, you will set a lower resistance and shorter time. By the end of a 12-week period (for some shorter; others longer) you should be able to exercise at or close to a sufficient pace to maintain the 20 minutes of sustained target pulse rate and with a frequency of three or four times each week.

Practical schedules for reaching this level are shown on Charts A (for walking) and B (for cycling) covering age levels from 50 to

Getting Started

79. Pay particular attention to the Pulse Limit columns. Your pulse should never surpass that level. If it does, you either are walking too fast or have too much resistance set on the stationary cycle.

Remember to take your pulse several times during your workout and just prior to the end. After a few weeks, you will be able to accurately estimate the exercising intensity necessary to reach and maintain the correct target rate indicated on the chart.

Chart A—A Walking Program
Age 50-59

Week	Distance (miles)	Time* (min.)	Frequency (per week)	Pulse Limit (age 50-54)	Pulse Limit (age 55-59)
1	1.5	30	4	105	100
2	1.5	28	4	105	100
3	1.5	26	4	110	105
4	2.0	36	4	110	105
5	2.0	35	4	110	105
6	2.0	34	4	115	110
7	2.0	32	4	115	110
8	2.0	31	4	115	110
9	2.5	39	4	120	115
10	2.5	38	4	120	115
11	2.5	37	4	125	120
12	2.5	36	4	125	120

*The time for walking programs includes the five or ten minutes it may take to bring your heart rate up to the pulse limit set

Age 60-69

Week	Distance (miles)	Time* (min.)	Frequency (per week)	Pulse Limit (age 60-64)	Pulse Limit (age 65-69)
1	1.0	20	4	100	95
2	1.0	19	4	100	95
3	1.0	18	4	105	100
4	1.5	29	4	105	100
5	1.5	28	4	105	100
6	1.5	27	4	110	105
7	2.0	38	4	110	105
8	2.0	36	4	110	105
9	2.0	34	4	110	105
10	2.5	43	4	115	110
11	2.5	42	4	115	110
12	2.5	40	4	117	110

Age 70-79

Week	Distance (miles)	Time* (min.)	Frequency (per week)	Pulse Limit (age 70-74)	Pulse Limit (age 75-79)
1	.75	15	4	92	90
2	.75	14	4	92	90
3	.75	13	4	96	94
4	1.0	20	4	96	94
5	1.0	19	4	96	94
6	1.0	18	4	97	95
7	1.5	29	4	105	100
8	1.5	28	4	105	100
9	1.5	27	4	105	100
10	2.0	38	4	108	104
11	2.0	37	4	108	104
12	2.0	35	4	110	106

Getting Started

Chart B - Stationary Cycling Program
Age 50-59

Week	Speed mph/rpm	Time (min.)	Frequency (per week)	Pulse Limit (age 50-54)	Pulse Limit (age 55-59)
1	15/55	10	3	105	100
2	15/55	12	3	105	100
3	15/55	12	3	110	105
4	15/55	14	3	110	105
5	15/55	14	3	110	105
6	15/55	16	3	115	110
7	15/55	16	4	115	110
8	15/55	18	4	115	110
9	15/55	18	4	120	115
10	15/55	20	4	120	115
11	18/65	20	4	125	120
12	18/65	20	4	125	120

Age 60-69

Week	Speed mph/rpm	Time (min.)	Frequency (per week)	Pulse Limit (age 60-64)	Pulse Limit (age 65-69)
1	15/55	10	3	100	95
2	15/55	12	3	100	95
3	15/55	12	3	105	100
4	15/55	14	3	105	100
5	15/55	14	3	105	100
6	15/55	16	3	110	105
7	15/55	16	4	110	105
8	15/55	18	4	110	105
9	15/55	18	4	110	105
10	15/55	18	4	115	110
11	15/55	20	4	115	110
12	15/55	20	4	117	110

Age 70-79

Week	Speed mph/rpm	Time (min.)	Frequency (per week)	Pulse Limit (age 70-74)	Pulse Limit (age 75-79)
1	15/55	10	3	92	90
2	15/55	12	3	92	90
3	15/55	12	3	96	94
4	15/55	14	3	96	94
5	15/55	14	3	96	94
6	15/55	16	3	97	95
7	15/55	16	4	105	100
8	15/55	18	4	105	100
9	15/55	18	4	105	100
10	15/55	18	4	108	104
11	15/55	20	4	108	104
12	15/55	20	4	110	106

Note: Some cycles calibrate speed in mph; others in rpm, so use either column. For warm-up, cycle 3 minutes at 65 rpm or 18 mph with no resistance. For the workout, set resistance at a point that will produce a pulse rate no higher than the one listed (some individuals may find using an RPM of 65 with a slightly lower resistance setting is preferable.) To cool down, cycle 3-5 minutes at the end of the workout with no resistance.

BODY STRENGTHENING

Your walking or cycling programs, in addition to supplying the necessary aerobics, also provide general exercise for your legs and lower torso. But the overall body, and especially the upper body and arms, need specific conditioning. The purpose is not to build exceptional muscles, but to increase the strength, endurance and flexibility of the body. The nine exercises described here are designed to accomplish this efficiently and safely.

The concept is one of exercising without strain, using small

Getting Started

weights for certain exercises plus multiple repetitions and then increasing the weight slowly over the 12-week period. Note the following caution: If you have any musculo-skeletal problems such as osteoporosis, osteoarthritis or other joint disease, low back and/or neck pain, review these exercises with your doctor or physical therapist to assure they are safe and appropriate for you.
This program was developed by the Virginia Sportsmedicine Institute (Robert P. Nirschl, M.S., M.D., Medical Director, and Janet Sobel, R.P.T., Director of Physical Therapy).

Each exercise focuses on a key body area. The effectiveness of an exercise, however, depends greatly on correct form and a consistent program. Proper posture, smooth movements and a correct raise, hold and lower rhythm are as important as the exercise itself. The following guidelines are pertinent. Learn them before you begin.

Posture

Good posture while doing the exercises is critical. The back should be flat with stomach tucked in. Slumped shoulders and/or a sway back will negate the exercise benefit and may even induce strain. If you are too tired to stand correctly, you are too tired to benefit from exercising.

Exercise Form and Technique

It is important to lower the weight more slowly than raising it because the muscle works harder (1) as it controls the lowering motion against gravity's pull, and (2) as it lengthens (lowering) rather than as it contracts (raising). This technique is protective of the joint. Raise during two counts (about 2 seconds), hold for two counts and lower in three counts. Inhale as you raise; exhale as you lower.

Determining Starting Weight

Although the average starting weight is one pound for women and two pounds for men, the following guide will establish your correct starting weight for each exercise. If you can easily and comfortably do more than 30 repetitions, then increase the starting weight by two pounds. If you can easily and comfortably do 15 repetitions, then increase the starting weight by one pound. If you can easily and comfortably do 10 repetitions, then stay at the average starting weight. If you are unable to complete 10 repetitions, do the exercise without any weight until you are able to do 15 repetitions comfortably.

Repetitions and Weight Gradations

Do each exercise in a complete set of 12 to 15 repetitions (except as noted.) When you can handle 15 repetitions comfortably for two sessions in a row, increase the weight by 1 pound for that exercise and cut back to 12 repetitions, increasing again to 15 when comfortable. Keep repeating this weight increase process.

You will be able to perform some of the exercises more easily than others, so increase weight independently for each exercise. There is an end point — a weight beyond which you cannot comfortably go. Stay with this weight. Do not push to extend it. (This will likely be 3-6 pounds for women and 5-8 pounds for men, but there is no minimum or maximum that must be achieved.)

Exercising
Frequency

Maximum benefit occurs through a regular and consistent program of exercise. This should be done every other day with a three-time minimum per week. Do not over-exercise to make up for a missed session or longer absence.

Warm-up
Before Exercise

Warm-up is essential to decrease injury potential to your tissues. By warm-up, we mean light activity to increase your body temperature. This can be done by easy cycling, slow jogging in place or brisk walking. Three to five minutes of warm-up is generally adequate for achieving the light sweat desirable.

Getting Started

UPPER AND LOWER BODY STRENGTHENING EXERCISES

1. Shoulder Circles
Exercise Benefits: Chest, Shoulders, Arms
Starting Position: Stand with feet comfortably apart, head up, trunk straight, buttocks tucked under and abdomen firm. Arms should be extended to the side and slightly forward, just below shoulder level.
Exercise Action:

   A. Palms down, rotate arms in backward motion 10 to 15 times. Begin with small circles and increase the circumference of circles as the exercise progresses.

   B. Repeat with palms up.

   C. Relax arms at side

   D. Repeat exercise.

NOTE: This exercise is done without weights at all times.

2. Horizontal Front And Side Lift
Exercise Benefits: Deltoid, Shoulder Girdle and Upper Chest
Starting Position: Stand with feet comfortably spread, arms at side and holding dumbbells.
Exercise Action:

   A. Slowly lift the dumbbells forward in front of you and hold for 2 seconds.

   B. Slowly move arms out to side position and lower to the starting position.

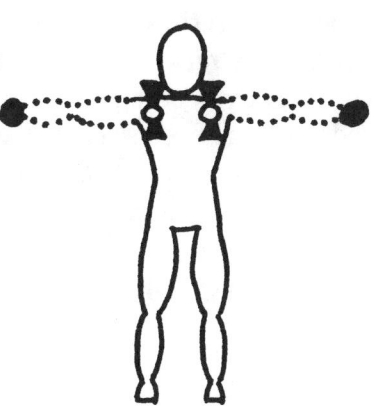

3. Military Press

Exercise Benefits: Shoulder Girdle, Chest, Upper Back and Arms

Starting Position: Stand with feet in balance and comfortably apart. Hold dumbbell in each hand, with palms forward, at shoulder level. Hold abdomen from and chin tucked in.

Exercise Action:

A. Raise right arm fully overhead.

B. Lower right arm to starting position while raising left arm to overhead position.

C. Keep repeating.

4. Bicep Curl

Exercise Benefits: Wrist Flexors, Biceps

Starting Position: Stand comfortably in balance with weight in each hand, palms facing forward, with back of hands against thighs. Keep abdomen and back straight and firm throughout.

Exercise Action:

A. Slowly raise right hand to shoulder level by bending elbow up. Keep abdomen and back straight and firm.

B. Slowly lower right hand to starting position while simultaneously raising left hand to shoulder level.

C. Keep repeating.

Note: This exercise can be done while sitting.

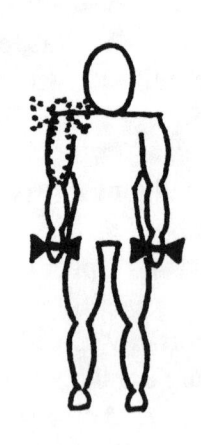

Getting Started

5. Sitting Hip Raise
Exercise Benefits: Hip Flexors
Starting Position: Sit on bench or table, legs dangling with knees at 90-degree angle, weight attached above the ankle. Hold edge of bench firmly with hands. 
Exercise Action:
   A. Raise thigh slowly to bring knee 10 inches off the surface while lower leg continues to hang straight down.
   B. Slowly lower to starting position. Do not raise hip off the table or bench during the exercise.
   C. Repeat with other leg.

6. Straight Leg Raises
Exercise Benefits: Hip Flexors and Quadriceps (front thigh)
Starting Position: Place weight above ankle of leg to be exercised. Lie on back with exercise leg straight. Bend knee of opposite leg and place foot firmly flat on the bench or floor.
Exercise Action:
   A. Bend foot up, tighten knee and slowly raise leg about 18 inches. Do not arch back.
   B. Lower leg slowly to starting position.
   C. Repeat with other leg.

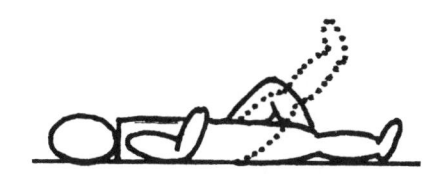

7. Calf Raise
Exercise Benefits: Plantar Flexors, Calf
Starting Position: Stand with good posture.
Exercise Action:
  A. Slowly raise up on tip-toes.
  B. Slowly return to starting position.
  C. Repeat 30 times.
  Note: This exercise and #8 & #9 below are always done without weights.

8. Pelvic Tilt
Exercise benefits: Abdominal muscles that support back.
Starting Position: Lie on your back with knees bent and feet flat on the floor.
Exercise Action:
  A. Press the small of your back against the floor and tighten your stomach and seat muscles (this should cause your pelvis to rotate forward).

  B. Hold the position for three seconds. Relax. Repeat 5 times.

9. Pelvic Tilt And Walk
Starting Position: Lie on back, knees bent and feet flat, hands clasped behind head, chin tucked in.
Exercise Action
  A. Tighten lower abdominal muscles to flatten the lower back against the floor.

B. Hold the back flat and walk the heels down along the floor. Straighten the legs as much as possible while keeping the back flat. Walk knees back to the bent position. Repeat 5 times.
Note: Go only as far down with the legs as you can without allowing the back to arch.

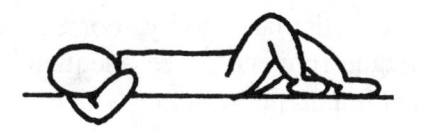

FLEXIBILITY

The role of flexibility in overall fitness and conditioning has been debated over the years. Individual perceptions vary, partly because of misconceptions surrounding this word. The following points apply:

Stretching And Warm-Up

Although flexibility and warm-up are two distinct processes, they are commonly confused. Warm-up is an increase in body heat to a light sweat resulting in less friction between the tissues. Warming up heats the gelled ground substances that are interspersed between the muscles, tendons and ligaments, thereby enhancing smooth, lubricated gliding of tissues. Flexibility exercise is the process of stretching muscles, ligaments and tendons. Warm-up must precede to minimize injury from the stretching process itself.

Does everyone need stretching exercises? Not always. Some are simply more flexible than others. In fact, some individuals have plenty of joint mobility and further stretching could easily invite lessened joint stability. Your own skeletal architecture should influence your flexibility goals. A hyperflexible joint — one that is too loose — can be just as vulnerable to injury as a hypoflexible (too tight) joint.

Which Areas Need Stretching?

Certain body areas tend to be tight in all individuals because of our life style. Most common are hip flexors and shoulder internal rotators. Too many years of constant slouching and sitting, along with reduced upper body exercise, leaves our shoulder and hip areas tight. Other body areas can become tight as a result of constant strengthening for a particular activity. For example, overly tight hamstrings can plague runners. Since adequate stretching of any area takes time, it is important to isolate which muscle groups need that kind of work.

Will Maximal Stretching Protect Against Injury?

On the contrary, maximal stretching in isolation can be counter productive. As Dr. Nirschl puts it, "Analysis of tendon rupture and muscle pulls reveals that most occur when the muscle is contracting (e.g., the overall tendon unit is shortening). Achilles tendon injury occurs at push off, not when the foot is being stretched up. Or, the usual hamstring pull occurs when the knee is bending, not being straightened. In short, injury does not occur by outside stretching force, but by intrinsic muscle contractile overload."

STRETCHING EXERCISES

Although the aerobics and upper body strengthening you will be doing to develop base-line fitness will not overload your muscles, ligaments or joints, this does not mean that appropriate stretching will not be useful or advisable. The following exercises will meet these flexibility needs. They should only be done after proper adequate warm-up and also are more effective following your aerobic and/or body exercises. In each exercise, stretch as far as you can short of pain. Hold six seconds. Then inhale deeply and, as you exhale, stretch a bit further, still without generating pain. Hold this fully stretched position for 10 seconds, breathing easily. Relax. Repeat 3 times.

Getting Started

1. Hamstring Stretch
Exercise Benefits: Hamstrings and calf muscles
Starting Position: Lying on back with both knees bent and feet flat.
Exercise Action:
　A. Straighten exercise knee, bringing leg toward trunk. Use hands to gently give extra stretch.
　B. Bend toes toward face to stretch calf.

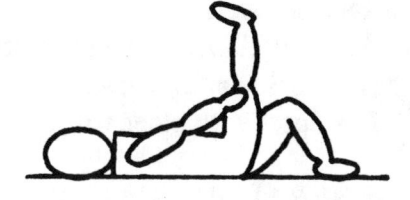

2. Knee Chest Flex
Exercise Benefits: Back Flexion
Starting Position: Lie on back with legs outstretched.
Exercise Action:
　A. Bend knees toward chest. Grasp knees with hands and slowly pull into chest.
　B. Hold this position while rolling back and forth 6 to 10 times.

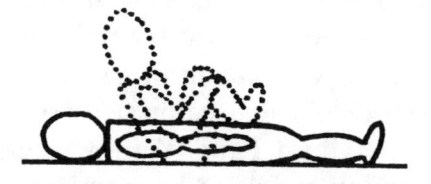

3. Tricep Stretch
Exercise Benefits: Triceps
Starting Position: Stand with good posture.
Exercise Action:
　A. Place exercise arm as far overhead as possible and bend elbow. Grasp above the elbow with free hand and gently pull the exercise elbow toward center of back.
　B. Repeat with other arm.

4. Horizontal Aduction Stretch
Exercise Benefits: Posterior Capsule (Back of Shoulder)
Starting Position: Stand with good posture.
Exercise Action:
   A. Bend elbow of exercise arm and pull the arm across front of chest.
   B. Repeat with other arm.

GENERAL PRECAUTIONARY NOTES

Although the aerobics, body strengthening and flexibility exercises recommended here have been designed for safety and performance without strain, there is no substitute for your own good judgment. Keep in mind the following basic precautions:

Old Injuries: Injuries that never have been fully rehabilitated can leave that part of the body vulnerable. Their status should be checked before starting exercises.

Chest Pain While Exercising: Any angina-type chest pain during or following exercises warrants immediate evaluation by your doctor. The symptoms are:
   A. Chest pain under breast bone or on the area around the heart during physical activity.
   B. Pain may radiate:
      1. To the left shoulder and down the left arm;
      2. To the back;
      3. Into the throat, jaws or teeth.
   C. This type of pain has been described as:
      1. Heaviness, oppressive;
      2. Tightness, crushing;
      3. Pressure, squeezing;
      4. Intense
   D. The pain lasts for several minutes.

3. Hereditary Factors: Such factors as poor leg alignment or other musculo-skeletal inherited weaknesses also need to be con-

Getting Started

sidered. In most cases, these will not prevent an exercise program, but you first should obtain orthopedic advice.

4. Warming Up: Walking by itself is a warm-up activity as is slow jogging in place or cycling a stationary bike without any resistance. A 3-5 minute warm-up before exercising is essential to decrease injury potential. You have warmed up adequately when you've achieved a light sweat.

5. Cooling Down: While this applies chiefly to those involved in very intensive exercises, it always is an important consideration. Many like to finish a workout with a burst of extra speed. This can be helpful for quickness and agility, but remember to then take time to cool down. Three to 5 minutes at a slow place should accomplish this. Stopping immediately after intensive exercise can cause dizzy spells, fainting or more serious consequences. Also, after a 3-5 minute cooling down period, your heart rate should have returned to below 95 (if training rate is over 100.) If it hasn't, this is a cautionary signal that should be checked out with your doctor.

Self Knowledge

The above points should not alarm you. They should, however, remind you to think about your body intelligently. Your exercise program should not strain or stress you, so don't rush and don't ignore signs of pushing too hard. You have time to improve your fitness. The best program is one that is regular and sensibly paced to fit your level of fitness.

Chapter IV
Seniors Competition

Before you skip this chapter, thinking it only for the die-hard jocks or those who are just trying desperately to recapture their youth, consider this: The majority of individuals who compete in senior sporting events are relative newcomers to that competition. They are not former champions or skilled athletes and, in most cases, were not involved in that sport or highly competitive when younger. So what is the attraction now? What is so different or special about sports competition among the seniors?

As you might suspect, there is no single answer. If you listen to the seniors who participate, though, the attraction centers around the following elements.

Enjoyable Camaraderie

It may surprise you, but senior events focus more on the fun of healthy competition than on the achievement of winning. First place is a nice experience, but winning, per se, has limited importance; "Number One," is really an empty phrase for seniors. There are no losers in seniors competition, because no one is there who does not truly enjoy that sport and who does not feel fortunate to be participating. It is the sharing of common interests, techniques and new developments within the sport that add up to the enjoyable camaraderie. In effect, the competitive event becomes part of the overall experience, not the essence of it.

Skill Development

Think about this factor, too. Its significance is greater than you might expect. Anyone who plays a sport delights in that unique surge of pleasure that flows momentarily when executing a particular action of the sport just right. Generally, though, this happens rather infrequently, and we lose it quickly simply because our skill level is limited.

To improve skill, one must isolate and correct shortcomings as well as learn and master new techniques. Interestingly, competition provides an especially valuable opportunity for achieving this, often proving more productive than hours spent in routine practice (during which we may also unknowingly practice the same mistakes and thus solidify them, which makes it that much more difficult to subsequently eliminate such errors).

Remember also that, in most sports, there really is no single correct motion that is just right or fits everyone equally well. Differences in anatomy such as short or long torso and trunk, short or long arms or legs affect the way each person best coordinates body movements. During competition, you can watch others of your general physique — some with less skill, others with more — perform under equal conditions. You will see examples of your own errors as well as ways in which your execution can be improved. The result is an excellent learning situation that can rapidly develop skills.

Incentive/Challenge

Don't kid yourself; incentive works at any age. You haven't read this far if you have eliminated incentive and challenge from your life.

"But," you say, "if winning isn't all that important, where's the incentive?"

Seniors Competition

Let's turn that around a bit. The act of winning may not be important, but the process of challenging oneself to do the best one can always generates a high personal return.

Look at it this way. If you play a sport regularly, you obviously enjoy it. So the question really is: Given your age and ability, (1) can you improve your performance skills; and (2) if you successfully accomplish this, will you enjoy the sport more? Rarely will there be a negative answer to either of these points.

The challenge sometimes is to improve conditioning (timing, quickness, flexibility and balance — not just strength and endurance — also benefit from improved fitness). Sometimes it is necessary to learn a new or an advanced technique. The incentive? Knowing you will experience more frequently that pleasurable feeling of good execution while also developing additional skill and competence. Together, these attributes enable you to gain even more satisfaction out of a sport you already enjoy.

With that introduction to seniors competition, you might wish to again review the sports described in Chapter II. Most of them offer such events, though you will find that the starting seniors age, and also the various age groupings designated, can differ with the sport. Basically, seniors competition within any sport commences at the point where competitive performance in that sport starts to drop purely due to the age factor.

That point, of course, can vary with the sport. In swimming, for example, it starts in the early 20s, while for racquet and most other sports, it commences around age 35. Seniors competition for small boat sailors (Sunfish), however, usually commences at age 45.

The racquet sports, skiing, boardsailing and most others then divide the subsequent years into five- or ten-year age classifications. With its long history of seniors competition, tennis separates seniors into five year age classifications. Boardsailing, which held its first National Seniors Championships in September, 1985, presently divides seniors into ten-year age groups. Not surprisingly, the top age for tennis now has crept up to 80 and over, while the newer sport of boardsailing currently lists 65 and over as its top age category. As a general rule, age categories will narrow and the top age will move higher as seniors competition expands within a particular sport.

Alpine skiing strongly promotes seniors competition through its NASTAR race program. These races against the clock are structured within various age classifications and are held at most ski resorts numerous times during the season. Individuals with the best times in regional races then have an opportunity to compete in the Nationals. NASTAR is highly organized and carefully supervised so that race courses fit the ability level of those competing.

Cross country skiing does not have the equivalent of NASTAR, primarily because cross country racing becomes very much a stamina sport that requires extensive training and conditioning. There is seniors competition within the U.S. and also internationally, but, for the most part, the participants are former racers.

Swimming, like tennis, has very active senior level competition, facilitated by the many community indoor and outdoor pools around the country, and also due, in part, to the fact that seniors competition starts at a relatively early age. The short hiatus between regular competition and the seniors tends to keep participants involved.

Although bicycle racing, like cross country skiing, is basically a stamina sport, it is beginning to attract more and more seniors, perhaps partially because it is one of the three triathalon sports and the "iron man" concept of the triathalon has received so much publicity. It is interesting to note, though, that the original iron man triathalon concept has now developed into the triathalon short course designed by the sport's promoters to be, "Manageable for the average fitness-conscious individual." The 0.9-mile swim, then 24.8-mile bike ride, followed by a 6.2-mile run, however, will be seen by most seniors as somewhat more demanding than the phrase "average fitness-consciousness" connotes. Nevertheless, the 1985 National Championship Short Course Triathalon included senior competitors in five-year age classifications commencing at age 35 and going up to 60 and over.

Rowers and canoers also are select groups. Those rowers involved in boat clubs have various types of local competition availa-

Seniors Competition

ble, but differing shell construction and sizes have handicapped, to some extent, the development of regular competition for seniors at the national level. This is rapidly changing, though, and races such as the Head of the Charles, in Boston, attract seniors from all over the country. Time handicaps are set for each competitor based on his or her age.

Canoe racing is a very selective and demanding stamina sport. Racing is in singles and pairs, and with different techniques from those described in Chapter II. These can be learned by an enthusiast whose fitness and conditioning allow the physical stress involved, but it becomes a different sport.

One of the most active sports for seniors competition is small boat sailing and particularly the international Sunfish class. There are no graduated age classifications; 45 and older is it. Competition is active throughout the U.S., with top regional performers also qualifying for the Nationals.

As the preceding summaries demonstrate, each sport organizes seniors competition with its own standards and rules, and even these sometimes can differ regionally within the same sport. Seniors competition is still a relatively recent development for most sports however, so refinements and changes are constantly under consideration, providing participants excellent opportunities to share in and help shape the way seniors competition develops in their sport.

Remember, too, that organizing and managing such events requires a lot of work, almost all of it performed by volunteers. One of the best ways to learn more about a sport is to participate in the organizing of competitive events. You not only will acquire a more thorough knowledge of that sport's rules, procedures and technical considerations, but will better understand, when competing yourself, how much planning and hard work go into a well run event.

Seniors competition will develop best in those sports whose participants are willing to share in all phases of its seniors program (and attracting more senior women into competition should be a key objective for every sport). Competitors need to know and appreciate the range of responsibilities involved in organizing and managing competitive events. Organizers need to understand the differing requirements and expectations of seniors, as opposed to younger competitors. By participating in instructional clinics for beginners, senior competitors also have wonderful opportunities to put something back into a sport that has provided them such pleasure. It is hard to find a more rewarding experience than that.

The concept of seniors competition still is in its infancy. Think back 10 or 15 years. Who knew about or noticed Senior Olympics in the 1970s? Yet, 43 states throughout the U.S. were holding such events annually by 1987, and the first National Senior Olympics was held June 27 through July 2, 1987, at St. Louis, Missouri. Sponsored by the new U.S. National Senior Olympics Foundation, competition included a broad range of track and field events, plus archery, cycling, bowling, golf, horseshoes, swimming and volley ball.

A far less competitive and more recreational sports concept stimulated founding of the National Senior Sports Association (NSSA). Located at 317 Cameron Street, Alexandria, Virginia 22314, the NSSA conducts recreational and competitive tournaments in tennis, bowling, golf, fishing and other sports at various resort locations. Its members are, "Individuals 50 years of age or older who want to maintain and improve physical and emotional health through sports participation."

In August, 1985, the philosophy of organized senior sports became international with the inauguration of the first world Masters Games at Toronto, Canada. The concept of bringing together senior sports enthusiasts from around the world every four years was developed by Dr. Maureen O'Bryan, Ph.D., currently president of the International Board of Directors of the world Masters Games. The major objective is to develop and promote the ideal of sport for life by demonstrating the wide number of individual and team sports (22 were selected for the first Games) that can be played competitively by both men and women well into advanced age. Masters, rather than seniors or veterans was selected to describe the event since it seemed to connote a wider age range.

The first Masters Games were a distinct success. More than 6,000 individuals, many from distant countries, journeyed at their

Seniors Competition

own expense to participate. There were some former champions and recognized top athletes among the competitors, but the majority were those who came for the sport, the camaraderie and the fun of international competition within their age groups. Thus, the focus clearly was on the quality of friendly competition, not on the super skill of a few elite athletes.

The 22 sporting events selected for this first Masters undoubtedly will have some changes based on experience and as different cities around the world host this event in subsequent years. All of the sports reviewed in Chapter II, however, with the exception of skiing (The Masters is a summer event), also are expected to be included in the next Masters Games, which will be held in Copenhagen in 1989.

But if you are just taking up a sport as a senior and never have competed in athletic events, is it realistic to consider seniors competition? The answer, unequivocally, is yes. Just keep your expectations equally realistic. The whole point of seniors competition is personal involvement and enjoyment at all levels. Whatever sports you select, whatever your age, you will find some individuals who perform better and some who are not as good you. Above all, remember that age is no barrier to learning any of these sports and developing your skills.

Certainly, before entering a competitive event, you should know the rules of the sport and have some basic skills, but it is a mistake to shy away from competition because you don't feel you are good enough at the sport. Remember that competition increases your rate of skill improvement and also helps you to get even more enjoyment out of the sport.

Nor does competition have to increase the physical exertion you normally experience in that sport. To be sure, it can add an incentive for improving your fitness, but we hope that's part of why you are reading this, anyway!

On the contrary, if you are fit enough to play the sport, you are fit enough to compete. If seniors competition in that sport means subjecting yourself to new and/or excessive physical strain, then something is very wrong with the way the event was organized and being managed. You also may have selected the wrong sport, or perhaps you have been unwilling to condition yourself in the first place. Your body is a marvelous structure. Even at advanced age, it retains the capacity to significantly improve its functioning level. All it needs is your determination.

It is no exaggeration that once you start competing, you quickly will recognize the appropriateness of the concept behind the Masters Games — "Sport for Life"!

Chapter V

Women And Sports

Why don't more women 50 and over participate in athletic sports? True, the percentage of participating men in this age category is not large, but for women, it is minimal. Given the fact that average life expectancy for women is approximately eight years longer than for men, and that good fitness dramatically improves the quality of life beyond 50, sports participation and its role in fitness ought to interest women as much as men, if not more.

But, although involvement in active sports is the ideal way to move toward better fitness habits, is it realistic to expect women 50 and over to become sufficiently concerned about fitness to develop interest in sports participation? Even more pertinent, since most women of this age had relatively little involvement in athletic sports at school and college, is it practical, or even possible, for them to commence now?

While these two questions are related, lack of interest in fitness is not the major barrier it might have been a few years ago. The medical profession, increasingly concerned about health maintenance for women in the middle and older age brackets, now strongly recommends exercise for this group. No, the problem is not lack of interest in fitness, (and the attention devoted to this subject by most women's magazines would seem to be further evidence of this). The major obstacle is that most women in this age category not only have little practical experience in sports, but from youth onward, were oriented away from athletic activities due to existing social mores and pressures.

At the very least, this now presents a large psychological hurdle, particularly when compared with similar aged men whose athletic exposure and involvement when younger facilitates a later re-entry into sports and conditioning programs. So, it is not surprising that many women have said to themselves, "Why should I even think about sports participation? I wasn't encouraged to learn sports and seldom had a chance to play them when young. It would be impossible for me to learn them now." Unfortunately, there are numerous men, in this age category who still think women should not be playing sports.

Beyond this significant psychological barrier is the fact that most women 50 and over have paid insufficient attention to their musculo-skeletal system from the age of 30, the very age at which everyone's physical functioning capacity commences to decline. As a result, considerable muscle atrophy, along with ligament and tendon weakness, may have occurred through disuse. Also, depending upon one's genes, physique and nutrition habits, some weakness of bone structure may have taken place due to the disease osteoporosis.

With that kind of discouraging picture, you may think, "Why discuss this further?" But listen to the good news. Current medical opinion has concluded that *fitness can be dramatically improved at any age!*

To put it another way, your body is ready to reverse poor fitness habits when you are. If, today, you are looking at arm, leg and stomach muscles that have become slack and weak through disuse, you can significantly alter that condition. Moreover, if you presently are free from the debilitating effects of osteoporosis, today's nutrition knowledge, plus exercise, allows much better protection against subsequent damage from this disease.

So, assuming your cardio-vascular system is basically healthy and your musculo-skeletal system is intact (no major joint damage), you can easily start the kind of conditioning program that will prepare you for enjoyable participation in a variety of sports and enable you to develop appropriate fitness for your age.

Obviously, if you have not run, skipped, tossed a ball, bicycled or swum from time to time during the past 20 years or more, your body coordination (not just your fitness) will have suffered. Your new conditioning program, however, will do more than increase your overall physical capacity and endurance. Other key functions such as balance, agility, coordination and body control also will start to improve. The progress will seem inconsistent, yet it will be taking place even when you can't notice it.

To be realistic, don't expect immediate results. If fitness has been ignored for a number of years, that neglect demands a price. It will take a little time -- don't begrudge this. The very worst thing you can do is to jump headlong into an overly intensive conditioning program that your body is not able to tolerate. Beyond the inevitable pain, it could result in severe damage.

As stressed in Chapter III, a complete physical exam by your doctor is the first step. If your doctor does not outline a specific beginning exercise program for you, then use the one detailed in Chapter III. Its flexible design makes that program safe for the less athletic and poorly conditioned person, yet also suitable for those with past athletic background.

The key to success is to initiate a safe and balanced program that fits your existing physical status. Your chronological age, by itself, has relatively little bearing on the type of conditioning program you should follow. Everyone's body has different characteristics. Each person has strong and weak points, unequal upper and lower torso relationships, and differing patterns of use. It is important to become sensitive and knowledgeable about your body. Don't try to emulate someone else's pace or type of conditioning exercises. Stick to your program.

Your doctor may recommend, as we do, that you commence with a modest program of walking or bicycling or swimming. As noted in the training schedules in Chapter III, you will keep increasing your pace and therefore the distance covered during the 12-week program. That training schedule has proven to be excellent for most beginners, but can be adjusted up or down to fit individual needs. Because you also will learn how to monitor your pulse before, during and after each exercise period, your conditioning program remains safe. It stays under your control at all times.

As a corollary to your walking or biking program (which satisfies your initial aerobic and lower torso conditioning needs) you also should start the program described in that same chapter as "Light Exercise" for the upper body. Again, consistency is the crucial element, combined with a level of physical effort that you are able to easily maintain. The basic concept here is repetitive exercise of selected muscle groups for short periods, without straining them.

There should be no discomfort or pain in performing any of the individual strengthening or stretching exercises. It is important to not move on to the next level of conditioning until you are comfortably doing the recommended maximum number of repetitions for any exercise at your starting level.

Assuming you also maintain sound nutritional habits, and are not significantly overweight to begin with (See Chapter VI for discussion of exercise and weight loss), this consistent exercise effort will greatly improve your fitness by the end of 12 weeks. In addition to a noticeable increase in pulmonary vitality (you won't get winded so quickly), important muscle tone will have returned throughout much of your body. You still will be missing some physical strength and endurance, but you certainly will be at a suitable level for safe and enjoyable sports participation.

Now, whatever sports you try, you can start with confidence in your body, and you will find this a significant psychological as well as a performing advantage. Some of the sports described in Chapter II offer considerable aerobic conditioning, others much less. Even if you combine an aerobic with a non-aerobic sport, remember to not stop your new focus on conditioning. You may well alter its emphasis in order to strengthen certain body areas important to those sports you are enjoying, but attention to basic conditioning should always remain.

And now that you can confidently try these fun sports, what lies ahead? What can you expect from your improved fitness and involvement in sports? Can you really learn those new sport skills, enjoy them, then develop more advanced techniques and even enter competitive events? Or must you limit yourself to remaining a beginner?

Well, it's really up to you and your motivation. Initially, you probably won't learn and improve your sport skills as rapidly as a teenager can, but you don't have to be far behind. In fact, you will find that a more mature and intelligent approach to learning a sport balances out the "I know it" attitude of confident youth.

At first, though, you should expect to experience somewhat rusty coordination, limited endurance and occasional strange body positions (which may be amusing to others, but not to you). That's right, be sure to bring along your sense of humor. Just as important, start your instruction in a program tailored to adults, not to youth. If you can talk a friend into starting with you, so much the better. Learning any sport has its frustrating moments, but if you have chosen a sport that appeals to your style, physical attributes and other interests, progress will come surprisingly fast.

Above all, don't be intimidated. You may be the oldest as well as the only woman in the class. Just remember to keep in mind that:

- All those in class probably are beginners too;
- Everyone there is trying to learn, not watch your mistakes;
- Other women your age (or older) have successfully learned this sport!

In a much shorter period than you now think possible, you will have developed the basic skills and be on your way to more advanced techniques. Since at least one of the sports you will have chosen is likely to offer fun competition for seniors, don't hold back from this additional and exciting dimension. And just about every sport mentioned in this book offers competitive events for women.

We're not suggesting that you should dedicate yourself to becoming a national or international competitor like Joan Paul, who took up biking in 1981 at age 48 and now is a top competitor in her age group (and placed fifth in the 1985 Veterans World Championships). That kind of goal may be the desire of some, but as Chapter IV emphasizes, it is the enjoyable camaraderie, exposure to new techniques, learning of additional skills, and the friendly challenge/incentive aspects that make these senior events so pleasurable and rewarding.

The other vital part of becoming involved in senior sports is to participate in the organizing of these events. This can be rewarding in several ways. First, you will learn a lot about the sports you enjoy. Second, your presence in the organizing as well as the competition end of senior sports will encourage more women to participate.

And that, in itself, is vitally important. Without more women participating in both aspects, senior sports competition will tend to remain too much a male fiefdom, lacking the flexible and innovative perspective needed to widen interest and broaden its scope. You are the person who can help add these important dimensions, but this cannot be achieved on the sidelines as a spectator. Only direct participation will provide women the knowledge, experience and influence to ensure that:

- Senior sports programs develop a broad and energetic organizing base of knowledgeable women and men;
- Senior events include recreational as well as elite competition;
- Support facilities are made attractive both to spectators and competitors;
- Local and regional events, not just national championship, are promoted and sponsored.

These are the kind of improvements that will enhance the impact of senior sports throughout our country. All that is needed is you. And you can't really lose when, along with your new fitness, you can enjoy sport for life!

Chapter VI
Nutritional Dangers: Supplements And Dieting

SUPPLEMENTS

Accurate and precise information regarding nutritional supplements is still hard to come by. Not that useful data is unavailable; the problem is separating the wheat from the chaff.

Even the professionals often disagree, and, recent changes in U.S. Government recommended daily allowances (USRDA) for vitamins testify to this. Today's more sophisticated focus on nutrition, particularly as this applies to those 50-and-older, is a relatively recent development. Not only has there been limited research in this arena, but, as Dr. Myron Winnick, M.D. (R.R. Williams Professor of Nutrition at Columbia University Institute of Human Nutrition) has pointed out, "Until 1980, there were no special nutrient requirements for older Americans. We just assumed the requirements for older Americans were the same as those for 18-year-old college students."

So it is no wonder that many of us remain perplexed about such specific questions as vitamin and mineral supplements. What's worse, the poor layman is constantly bombarded by the often conflicting advertising claims of the manufacturers of vitamin and mineral supplements. Their messages generally imply: "If you are feeling low on energy, you may be lacking that special ingredient our product contains."

The fact is that the market is literally awash with vitamin and mineral supplements, all competing with each other for your dollar. Without a Ph.D. in nutrition, it is practically impossible to know if one brand's "special supplements" actually provide a nutritional advantage or are just a marketing gimmick.

Should you worry about all this?

That depends. If you are taking vitamin and/or mineral supplements at your doctor's recommendation, that is obviously fine. If, however, you are in the large category of individuals who is taking supplements simply to ensure you are getting enough vitamins, it becomes complicated, possibly dangerous and certainly expensive. Reading the labels will be confusing to most and advertising claims are unreliable. There is also evidence that taking more than the USRDA levels can be harmful. Finally, vitamins are not cheap.

The Center for Science in the Public Interest (CSPI), a nonprofit public interest organization with headquarters at 1501 16th Street NW, Washington, DC, 20036, has provided a detailed review of vitamin and mineral supplements in its March 1986 newsletter, Nutrition Action. While that report covers only brand name suppliers of single pill nutrients (subsequent newsletters cover other aspects), even this limited summary will help you sift out which brands are more, rather than less, applicable for your requirements. CSPI also has provided the following useful summary clarifying the differences between RDAs (Recommended Dietary Allowances); USRDAs and MDAs (Minimum Daily Allowance):

"The national Academy of Sciences sets the RDAs. There are several RDAs for each vitamin and mineral; the allowance varies for males and females, for young and old.

"The Food and Drug Administration (FDA) sets a single USRDA for each nutrient, largely based on the RDA for teenage boys, the group that tends to have the largest need, except for pregnant women. The FDA requires nutrition labels on foods to disclose

Nutrititional Dangers: Supplements And Dieting

vitamin and mineral content as percentages of USRDA. The FDA can't force labels on supplements to use the USRDAs, but most suppliers do.

"The MDAs were forerunners of the USRDAs and are now out of date. Don't buy supplements that use MDAs instead of USR-DAs. The MDAs make the nutrient levels look higher, and unless you know the MDAs by heart, you'll have no way of knowing what you are buying."

In addition to the CSPI newsletter, other pertinent nutrition and health information can be obtained from the following:

Diet and Nutrition Letter, Tufts University School of Nutrition, 53 Park Place, New York, NY 10016

Health and Nutrition Newsletter, Columbia University School of Public Health, P.O. Box 5000-M, Ridgefield, NY 07657

Wellness Letter, The University of California at Berkeley, P.O. Box 10922, Des Moines, IA 50340

Mayo Clinic Health Letter, Mayo Medical Resources, Rochester, MN 55905

Harvard Medical School Health Letter, Subscription Dept., P.O. Box 10948, Des Moines, IA 50340

Each of the newsletters offers balanced and well documented information. Generally 8 to 14 pages in length, each issue will contain a feature article with shorter pieces covering related nutrition, diet and health topics. Quality newsletters are also published by other medical institutions with schools of public health.

DIET AND DIETING

As of publishing date, hundreds of books recommending specific diets are in print and available and the likelihood is that there will be many more to come! The seemingly endless market for such material is not hard to fathom; a significant percentage of Americans are overweight, know it, and are always looking for the magical diet, meaning one that will solve their weight problem but not restrict them from their favorite foods.

Because of heightened media focus on diet and nutrition, there is much more awareness today concerning the overall importance of a balanced diet and healthy foods. Conversely, the dangers of such habits as reliance on frozen foods alone, too many fast food menus, and frequent nibbling of high-fat content snacks, have now been well documented.

While the effect of diet on cardiovascular disease has been thoroughly established, more recent research also indicates possible links between diet and some cancers, though no hard statistics have been developed or accepted. Dr. Peter Greenwald, M.D., director of the Division of Cancer Prevention and Control at the National Cancer Institute (NCI), says that 35 percent of all cancer deaths may be related to the way we eat. This estimate is based on NCI's study of the international differences in diet and cancer occurrences. Dr. Greenwald points out that cancer rates vary markedly from country to country and that when people move to another country, their risk of cancer changes. As one pertinent illustration, he cites the fact that cancer of the colon causes three times more deaths in the U.S. than in Finland. Comparison of diets here and in Finland show that the biggest difference in diet is in the amount of fiber consumed. The Finns eat about twice the amount of fiber we Americans eat. Another example documents the effect of fat in the diet. Countries whose fat intake is about one half of the U.S. level have slightly below half the breast cancer mortality rate.

Yet, even if we accept the growing evidence that links diet to good health, this doesn't, by itself, resolve the overweight and dieting problems that affect so many Americans. Obesity recently has been defined by the National Institute of Health (NIH) as being more than 20 percent over the chart weight for your sex, height and body frame. In this instance, chart weight refers to those figures published in 1983 by the Metropolitan Life Insurance Co., and which are not related to age.

Nutrititional Dangers: Supplements And Dieting

Nevertheless, using that definition, some 30 million Americans are estimated to be obese! Most of us would probably consider "overweight" as being 10-15 percent over the chart weight with obesity describing only those significantly over that level. Dr. Jules Hirsch, M.D., chairman of the panel of doctors and nutritionists who met at NIH in 1985 and determined that the 20-percent-above-body-weight criteria constitutes an established health hazard, went on to say, "There's no one point at which obesity occurs. What we're telling people is that obesity is any excess fat and that the danger increases on a sliding scale."

That is excellent advice on what not to do, but what is the most effective way to lose weight? For the seriously overweight person — meaning obese — programs similar to that offered by the Duke Diet and Fitness Center at Durham, North Carolina, have proven effective by providing a combination of careful dieting, nutritional education, exercise and counseling. Some call this, "Behavior modification". However one chooses to describe the program, exercise has proven to be an imperative key ingredient. Those who attempt diet alone almost always fail. They lose weight for a short period and then subsequently regain what they lost and sometimes even more. At the Duke Center, those who successfully combine diet control with a commitment to exercise usually have a high rate of success.

A negative argument against any type of weight loss program evolves around the theory that individuals have a "set point" for their body weight, that this is established in early adulthood, and cannot be significantly altered thereafter. This theory argues that the body fights to stay at its set point, and that permanent weight reduction for the fat person is doomed. There is some evidence to support part of this theory; both the body and the mind indeed are reluctant to re-set and maintain the necessary discipline to achieve and maintain weight loss. However, the basic theory fails to account for the fact that in the year 1900, Americans were considerably leaner than today. Is it rational to conclude that the far less fatty diet of that era and the far greater amount of daily exercise then (due, at least partially, to no cars) were not factors in that thinner America?

For those in the overweight rather than obese category, there is strong evidence that exercise can play a vital role, not just in weight reduction, but in weight distribution. There is no single statistic that proves this. Rather, it is the accumulation of evidence from the many research projects currently examining the American overweight problem.

Dr. Peter Wood., M.D., associate director of the Stanford Center for Research in Disease Prevention, has reached some interesting conclusions about this topic. Despite the claim by some that exercise reduces appetite, his research has determined that, on the contrary, moderately overweight individuals who initiated and maintained a consistent exercise program, began to eat somewhat more, raising their caloric intake per week by about 15 percent. But — and this is the fascinating aspect — *they steadily continued to lose weight!*

The initial conclusion was they they were simply exercising away those additional calories. Surprisingly, additional study indicated that these individuals were eating some 300 more calories per day, equal to 2,100 more calories per week, yet were only burning off through exercise about 1,200 calories per week.

So how could there be weight loss? In fact, why wasn't there a weight gain?

One theory is that as they became more fit, they also became more active in other ways. They walked more instead of riding short distances by car, used stairs instead of elevators, etc. This tendency toward more activity in daily life undoubtedly explains some of it, but Dr. Wood has growing evidence that exercise also builds your basic metabolic rate, thus boosting the amount of calories your body burns, even hours after exercise.

Researchers don't agree on how long this effect lasts, since science has yet been unable to detect and measure small changes in the metabolic rate. It is clear, though, that even a minimal one percent increase in an individual's metabolic rate would burn a lot of calories over a 24-hour period. Nevertheless, what is important is not whether the increased metabolic rate lasts one or many hours after completing exercise; the exciting and encouraging fact is that in some way not yet precisely determined, calories do continue to be burned off for a period after exercise has stopped. This is a valuable bonus that will benefit anyone.

Have no illusions, though. A proper weight reduction plan is not a quick fix. A loss of two pounds per month is considered the maximum desirable rate. One pound is the usual goal. Dr. Wood has found that 20 minutes of aerobic exercise three times per week is sufficient for the moderately overweight person to maintain the one-pound-per-month loss, and he makes an important additional point. Losing excess pounds for the moderately overweight person admittedly can be achieved by diet alone for those who are disciplined. Exercise, however, burns the pounds you most need to lose — fat pounds. Dieting, on the other hand, tends to destroy muscle, not fat. According to Dr. Wood, even mild dieting — restricting caloric intake to about 1,800 calories per day — will diminish muscle if you do not exercise.

A potentially more serious problem from dieting is the effect on bone mass, particularly as this applies to women over 50 and their susceptibility to osteoporosis. Various amounts of calcium supplement are being recommended as a protection, but the determination of *how much* should be left to each individual's doctor. On the encouraging side, regular exercise has proven to be one of the best antidotes for preventing bone mass loss at any age.

There are differing views as to the amount of exercise that is appropriate for a weight reduction program. Drs. Leonard Epstein and Rena Wing, of the Western Psychiatric Institute and Clinic at Pittsburgh, Pennsylvania, analyzed all the published studies on exercise and weight loss and concluded that those who exercised four to five times per week lost weight about two or three times faster than those who exercised only three times weekly. This, however, would imply a faster rate of loss than most doctors would recommend.

In any case, for those with a weight problem, particularly the seriously overweight, it is clear that diet alone is not the answer and, unless one is under medical care, dieting may well have serious adverse effects. It is equally clear that exercise is critically important in any weight control program. The exercises in Chapter III, Getting Started, are fully applicable to this problem, but a preliminary and thorough physical examination is even more important for the overweight person beginning any exercise program. You need to know your true health status not only for safety reasons, but also to provide a valid starting point against which you can realistically measure your progress. If one or two pounds of weight loss per month seems insignificant to you, think of it in terms of 12 to 24 pounds in a year. Yes, that is about the time for re-visiting your doctor. That could be one visit you both will be happy about.

CHAPTER VII

Sports Medicine: The New Field of Injury Prevention

Ten years ago, sports medicine was a relatively new medical term describing a specialized orthopedic field, the development of which was initiated largely by the needs of the professional sports world. Focusing on the numerous types of serious musculo-skeletal damage experienced by these athletes, sports medicine rapidly generated techniques that have revolutionized the repair and rehabilitation of such injuries. Perhaps even more important, it has introduced injury prevention concepts that can apply to everyone and, in particular, to those of us over 50.

Sports medicine's remarkable "cures" naturally receive most of the headlines (repair of torn knee cartilage through arthroscopic surgery, allowing professional football players to be reactivated in a few weeks instead of being out for the season, is a good example).

But, as the best sports medicine practitioners always emphasize, surgery should be the last resort in the cure of musculo-skeletal problems. And, in our age category, musculo-skeletal malfunctions tend to increase. Yet, most of our neck, shoulder, upper/lower back, hip, knee and ankle problems can be dramatically improved — and often totally cured — through a proper rehabilitation program. The irony is that this cure generally comprises many of the strengthening techniques that, if practiced earlier and prior to the problem, might well have prevented its occurrence.

While arthroscopy may be helpful in some instances, it has limited application and is only one of many available techniques. On the other hand, everyone should and can benefit from the prevention side of sports medicine. To visualize the true importance of this concept, stop for a moment and think about the extraordinary musculo-skeletal system which links together your whole body.

Consider what happens, for example, when you simply throw a ball, or serve in tennis. If you make this throwing motion, you will see immediately that joints on both sides of your body are affected. Commencing with your toes and foot as you step forward and continuing through your ankle, knee, hip, lower and upper back, shoulder, elbow, wrists and finally, the fingers — and then finishing with your weight on the other leg — each joint plays a critical role. Weakness, limited motion or poor performance of one link in this chain inevitably affects the overall action and, if uncorrected, can lead to problems in a separate joint. Just injure your big toe and see how this affects your ability to throw!

When young, and even through most of our middle years, this marvelously linked and coordinated musculo-skeletal system performs so smoothly that we assume it will continue that way. Those who suffer injuries and crippling diseases like rheumatoid arthritis (or even the familiar osteoarthritis that many of us experience by our forties), know better. The connective tissues, cartilage, lubricating fluids, ligaments, tendons and muscles that support our joints also are affected by the way we age, not just by injury or disease. Quite logically, it is the weight-bearing joints that take the brunt of the wear and tear. Who do you know over 50 who has not undergone at least some discomfort with one or more of the neck, back, hip, knee or ankle areas?

Eventually, each of us experiences some of the symptoms. Stiffening of the joints, reduced range of joint motion, and even some soreness after extended exercise will, to a greater or lesser de-

Sports Medicine: The New Field Of Injury Prevention

gree, accompany the aging process. But, if you have conditioned the key muscles, ligaments and tendons that both protect and create good joint action, these symptoms will be minor, not major. Then as you enjoy your various sports, you will be promoting continued strong functioning of these vital joints as well as minimizing chances of injury.

Remember, you will be taking major strides toward this important objective by initiating the exercise program detailed in Chapter III, Getting Started. Your upper and lower body muscles will become better toned and the parallel stretching exercises will surely increase your general flexibility of motion.

Some may be content with that degree of conditioning activity. Many, however, will want to enjoy one or more of the sports described in Chapter II. Although you will be physically ready to learn and play any of these sports, you also are likely to expend increasing levels of energy as your skill advances. This is a healthy objective overall, but warrants additional conditioning.

To put it another way, the fun, enthusiasm and exhilaration generated by your increasing skill at a sport can subtly lead to extra physical stress on certain areas of your body. In Chapter II, we noted stress areas for each sport under the sub-section Fitness Level Needed and Injury Potential. Review those sections as your sports action increases.

The main body areas that need special attention are the lower back, the knees and ankles and (particularly for the racquet sports) the shoulders, elbows and wrists. These, of course, also are the same body areas that so often are injured simply in everyday accidents (slipping on wet pavements or floors; tripping over curbs; bending down too often; or lifting heavy loads improperly, etc.). In sum, all are vulnerable to such injuries. Strengthening these key body areas becomes important not just for sports enjoyment, but also to preserve the physical functioning capacity that is so essential to pleasurable day-to-day living.

The exercises described here were developed by Janet Sobel, R.P.T., director of physical therapy, the Virginia Sportsmedicine Institute, and have been tested and refined specifically for those 50-

and-over who already have attained the base-line fitness level described in Chapter III. Dr. Robert Nirschl's comments about joint mobility and strength further explain why these exercises are so important:

> "Leaving aside hereditarial factors, and assuming no injury to the joint over the years nor damage from a disease like arthritis, the articular surfaces (where the bones meet and their surfaces are cushioned and protected by cartilage) will not have changed significantly by age 50. In effect, the actual movement of the joint should still be un-hindered.
>
> "The usual problem is that poor muscular, ligament and tendon strength leaves the joint action unstable and weak and also can limit the range of motion that is possible, safe and/or comfortable. While the aging process does reduce muscle, ligament and tendon functioning capabilities, the most serious loss results from disuse. This kind of loss can be prevented by proper exercise.
>
> "Modern life (work as well as social) limits all around conditioning for most of us. Moreover, if we concentrate on just one sport, there's also a tendency to overuse one set of muscles, ligaments and tendons. So, there is a specific as well as a general need to strengthen the various body areas. Participating in several sports is advantageous in that this exercises a wide variety of muscles, ligaments and tendons — and will tend to prevent overstress of one part of the body. A person who completes the kind of exercise program noted in Chapter III, Getting Started, should be able to participate in the various sports recommended. Additional strengthening exercises will both increase that person's physical functioning capabilities and also minimize chances for injury."

Sports Medicine: The New Field Of Injury Prevention

THE IMPORTANCE OF SPECIALIZED STRENGTHENING EXERCISES

The linkage elements in our musculo-skeletal system facilitate and also complicate strengthening exercises for specific body areas. Knee joint function, for example, is not only affected by the muscles, ligaments and tendons immediately around it, but also by those in the upper and lower leg, both above and below the knee. Similar relationships occur in the other body areas noted.

Because this superb linkage system also allows us motion in so many directions — push/pull, lift/press, forward/backward, pivot left/right, bend up/down, etc. — strengthening any single area of the body requires a group of related exercises.

You also will note that each exercise grouping conditions the major antagonistic muscles in that body area, i.e., muscles whose actions tend to oppose and/or balance each other and which need to coordinate smoothly for efficient joint movement. The quadriceps and hamstrings of the upper leg are familiar antagonistic muscles to many of us, but there are other important sets of such muscles. Some of the major ones are illustrated in Diagrams A, B and C. What frequently happens is that a particular sport or activity exercises one of the related antagonistic muscles much more than the other. Bicycling, for example, emphasizes the "quads" more than the "hams," so the latter often need extra strengthening.

Failure to equalize conditioning of antagonistic muscles inevitably brings problems. At the least, it limits or weakens body motions. More worrisome, it can lead directly to imbalance and instability of the joint, and can often result in unnecessary injury.

Because each of us is constructed in differing proportions (short, strong legs for instance, vs. long, thin ones — with comparable differences in the upper torso), our body vulnerabilities also are likely to be different. But one area of the body is vulnerable for everyone. This is the back and particularly the lower back. No one can afford to ignore its care or be unaware of the constant stress it undergoes. The back's vulnerability stems from its complicated structure and demanding role.

The spinal, or vertebral, column which is comprised of

SPORTS AFTER 50

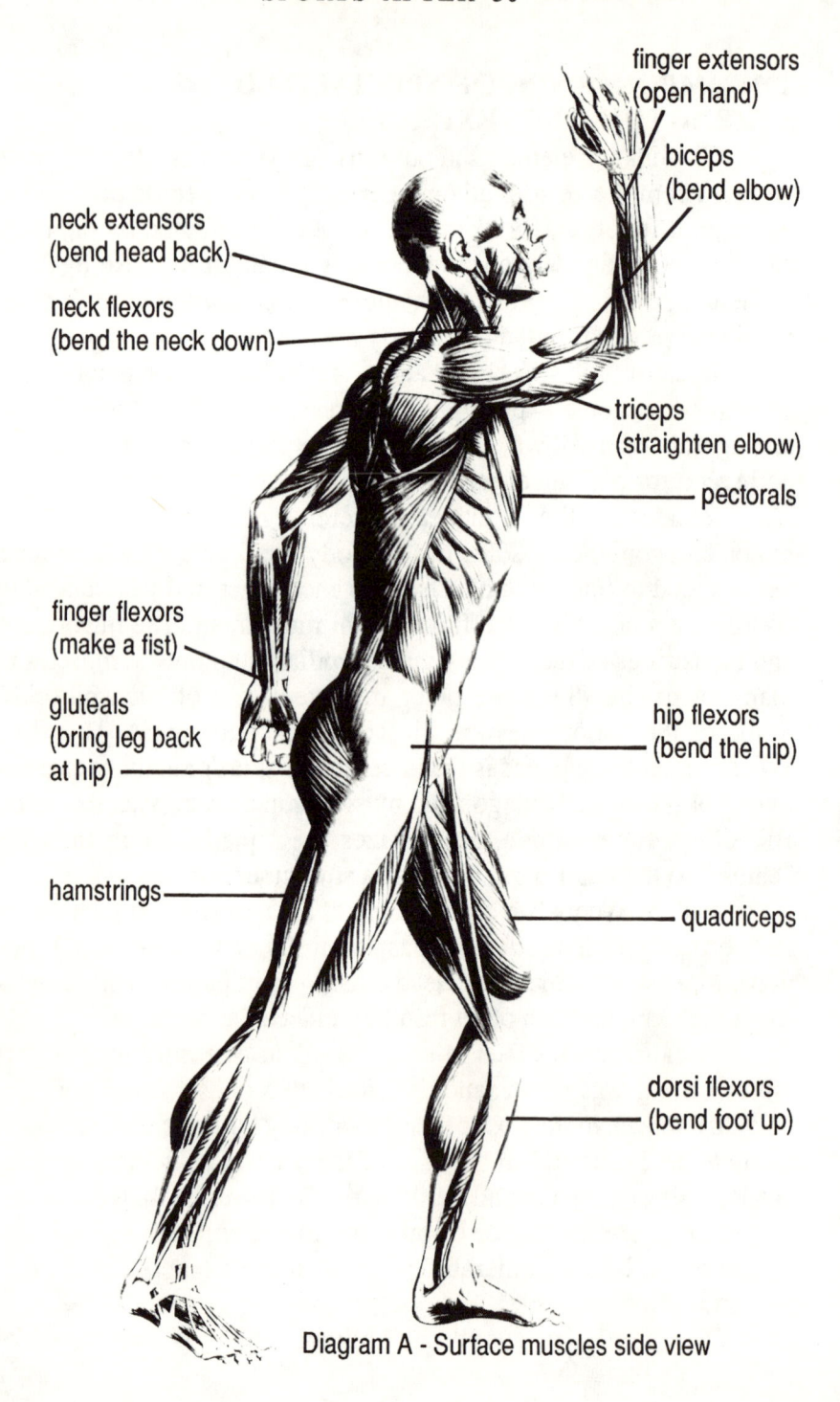

finger extensors (open hand)

biceps (bend elbow)

neck extensors (bend head back)

neck flexors (bend the neck down)

triceps (straighten elbow)

pectorals

finger flexors (make a fist)

gluteals (bring leg back at hip)

hip flexors (bend the hip)

hamstrings

quadriceps

dorsi flexors (bend foot up)

Diagram A - Surface muscles side view

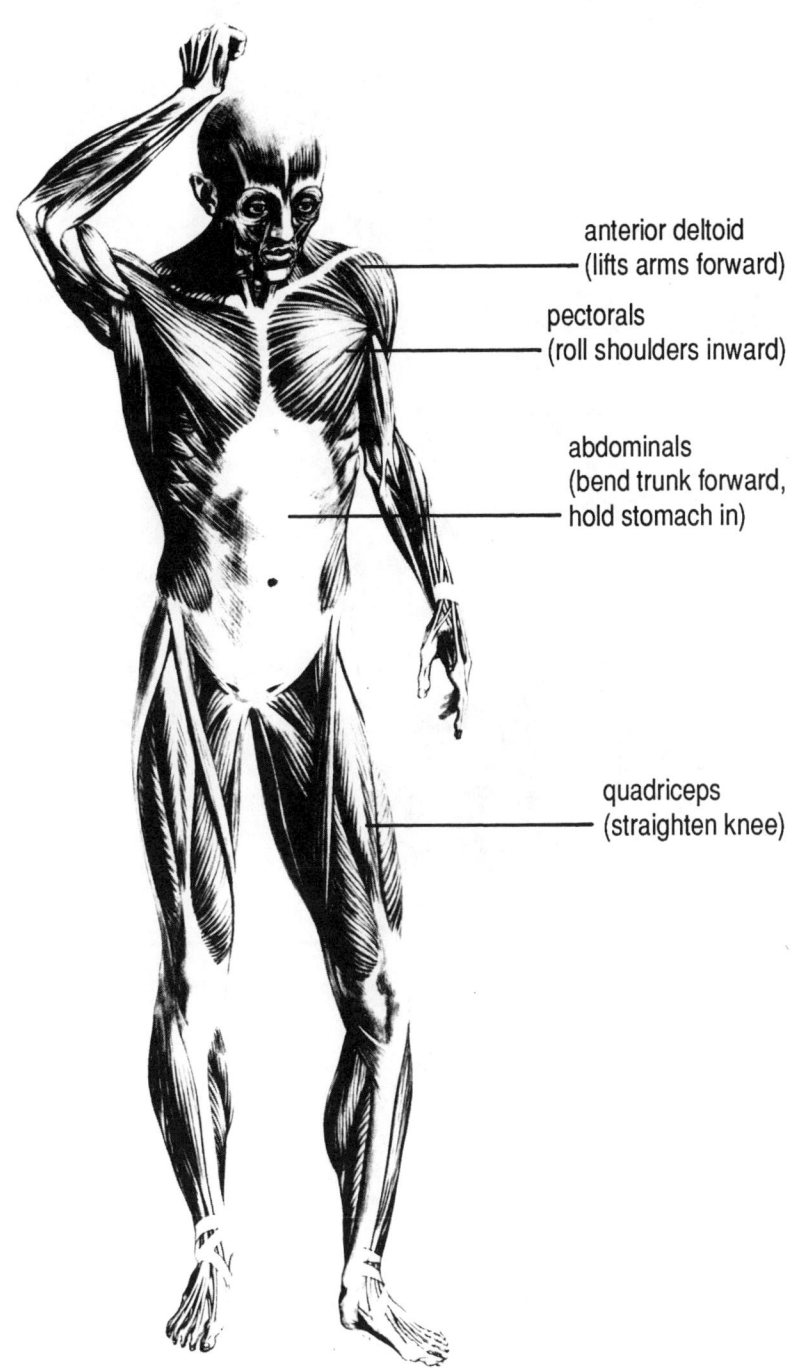

Sports Medicine: The New Field Of Injury Prevention

anterior deltoid
(lifts arms forward)

pectorals
(roll shoulders inward)

abdominals
(bend trunk forward,
hold stomach in)

quadriceps
(straighten knee)

Diagram B - Surface muscles front view

Diagram C - Surface muscles back view

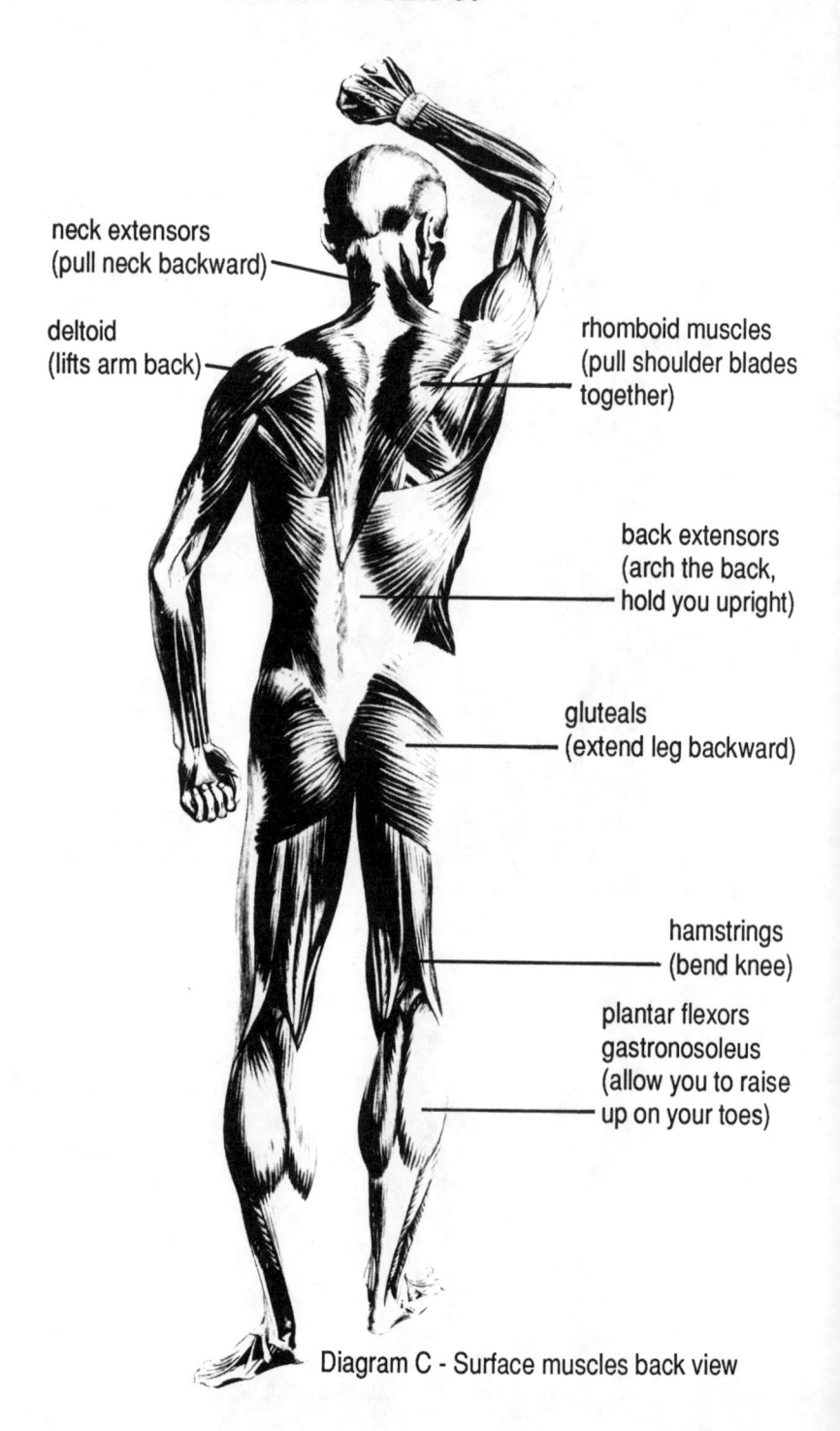

Sports Medicine: The New Field Of Injury Prevention

bones, ligaments, disks, muscles and joints, is intricately designed to support the body, yet must also allow the extensive motion of normal body activity. This inherent conflict between the need for back stability, on one hand, and wide mobility, on the other, lies at the root of the problem.

The spinal cord, fortunately, is relatively well protected within the vertebral column. The nerves, however, which originate from the spinal cord and extend throughout the body, are susceptible to injury as they exit the cord and intersperse themselves among the muscles, ligaments and tendons.

The musculature, which supports the sophisticated structure and arrangement of the vertebral column, also is complex. And, unlike the various limb muscles, many of which can be individually strengthened, the differing lengths, complicated function, deceptive locations and multiple layers of back muscles (especially those in the lower back) inhibit specific strengthening.

Finally, the lumbar (lower back) portion of this vertebral column and its supporting muscles not only must constantly bear the considerable weight of the upper body, but also endure tremendous extra stress whenever the body is not erect while standing. Two measurements illustrate how extensive these pressures can be. First, due to leverage, pressure on the disks in the lower lumbar vertebrae (just from bearing the weight of the upper body in an erect position) produces an effective load in the range of 200-300 pounds. Bend the body forward a mere 20 degrees while holding a 22-pound weight and this effective load jumps to 430-500 pounds!*

Given these tremendous pressures and loads, it is not surprising that the muscles of the lower back are frequently subject to stress and that the disks tend to lose their proper shape over time, protrude where they can press against nerves or can even be ruptured, which leads to much more serious complications. Fortunately, well-conditioned abdominal muscles can provide the assistance back muscles need to withstand their constant load.

*Functional Anatomy of Limbs and Back, W.H. Hollingsworth, Ph.D., W.B. Saunders Co., Philadelphia, Toronto, London · 1969

The conclusion, therefore, seems clear. First, correct posture is a key ingredient in protecting the back. Second, it becomes vitally important to strengthen the abdominal muscles. It is not the visually flat stomach that is important; it is the strength of the abdominal muscles underlying the surface. With the exception of lying on your back, gravity is forever pulling on the abdominal muscles, tending to loosen them and weaken their support of correct body position.

Strong abdominal muscles will hold the pelvis in its most advantageous position and allow the back muscles to function as efficiently as possible. It is this dynamic balance that is protective against injury because the abdominal muscles, when properly conditioned, also can absorb additional forces and stress that otherwise would be directed against the lower back.

By age 50, the lower back has experienced considerable wear and tear. Strengthening the full range of the abdominal muscles will, at a minimum, be a major and practical investment in preserving your comfort and mobility (if you have avoided lower back discomfort up to now, you are among a minority of lucky individuals). As a pleasant bonus, this step also will enable you to safely enjoy a variety of active sports and reduce the chances of stressing your lower back.

GENERAL INSTRUCTIONS

There are some basic considerations that apply to all these exercises in addition to the specific instructions noted for each exercise group and those affecting the individual exercises.

1. **Warm-Up:** As with the Getting Started exercises detailed in Chapter III, always warm up for 3 to 5 minutes before beginning.

2. **Proper Form:** Each exercise is designed to be executed in a certain way and in a specific body position. It must be performed that way to be effective and safe.

3. **Repetition:** Exercises are not a competition. The

Sports Medicine: The New Field Of Injury Prevention

"initial" and "progress to" numbers are simple guides. Always exercise well within your limits and increase repetitions only as you are comfortable.

4. **Exercise Frequency:** Three times per week is sufficient for any group. If you are doing more than one group during each exercise period, be sure to rest a day in between periods. Another approach is to perform each group on alternate days.

5. **Fatigue:** A few exercises, such as lateral step-ups, are not affected by weight resistance, so the instruction is: "Repeat to fatigue." This means exercise until the muscles in that area begin to be tired or you find you are not maintaining good form. Fatigue may affect a particular area but also may show up as inability to maintain good body posture in other body parts. Those parts are substituting to help out the exercise area. You must be aware of this because poor exercise form can result in unnecessary injury.

KNEE AND UPPER LEG EXERCISES; SHOULDER, ARM AND WRIST EXERCISES

Begin with no weight. Start with 12 repetitions, or as many as you can do without straining, and progress to 15 repetitions. Once you can comfortably do 15 repetitions for two consecutive exercise periods, add a 2-pound weight, go back to 12 repetitions and progress up to 15 again. When comfortable at 15 repetitions, increase the weight by one pound and follow the same procedure. Repeat this process until you reach a point at which additional weight requires straining. This is your "end point," and it will be different for each person and for different exercises.

Some exercises are done with no weight at any time. Others are sufficiently difficult so that it may take more time before you are ready to add the first weight. Some will be easy and weight can be quickly added. Do each exercise at the same rate: two counts to raise, two to hold, and three to lower.

KNEE AND UPPER LEG EXERCISES

1. Terminal Knee Extensions
Exercise Benefits: Quadriceps

Starting Position: Sitting on floor, knee bent to 30-45 degrees over a rolled towel or pillow. Place weight on ankle.
Exercise Action: Bend ankle up, straighten knee.
Note: This exercise also may be done sitting in a chair.

2. Sitting Straight Leg Raise
Exercise Benefits: Quadriceps and Iliopsoas (Hip Flexors)
Starting Position: Sit on the floor, exercise leg in front. Opposite leg bent with foot on the floor. Hands on floor by hips for support. 
Exercise Action:
   A. Bend up foot of exercise leg. Tighten knee and raise leg off floor about 12 inches. Keep knee straight. Try not to lean back.
   B. Slowly lower
Note: This exercise is done without weight at all times.

3. Hip Adductor Side Lift
Exercise Benefits: Groin and Inner Thigh
Starting Position: Position weight on ankle of exercise leg. Lie on your side with hips straight up. Rest upper leg on a chair seat. Use hands for balance.
Exercise Action: Slowly raise lower leg to highest position and return to starting position. Keep knees straight and pelvis in a straight up position.

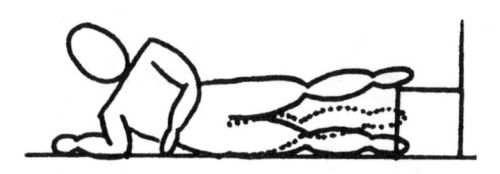

Note: Do not tilt back. Be sure inner thigh points toward ceiling.

4. Hip Abductor Side Lift
Exercise Benefits: Hip and Thigh abductors (Outer Thigh Muscles)
Starting Position: Lie on the floor or on a bench, on your side with the exercise leg on top. Use a small pillow or your arm to support your head. Use your other arm for balance and flex underneath leg at the knee to provide additional balance. Hang the weight at the ankle.
Exercise Action: Leading with the heel, slowly lift the leg as high as possible keeping the knee and pelvis straight at all times. Slowly lower the leg to starting position.

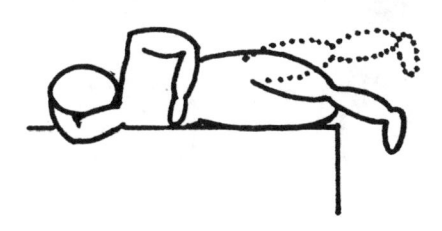

5. Knee Curls
Exercise Benefits: Hamstrings
Starting Position: Lie on stomach on the floor or a bench with pillow under abdomen. Position weight at the ankle.
Exercise Action: Turn fore foot inward. Slowly bend knee upward as far as possible, hold, then slowly lower. Do not let buttocks raise up.

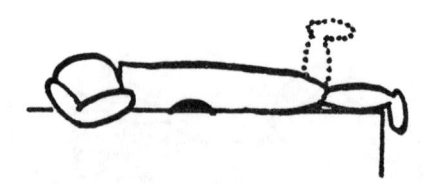

6. Lateral Step-Ups
Exercise Benefits: Quadriceps, Inner and Outer Thigh Muscles
Starting Position: Stand sideways with exercise leg next to step.
Exercise Action:
  A. Step up with the exercise leg, follow with opposite leg.
  B. Then step down with opposite leg, follow with exercise leg.

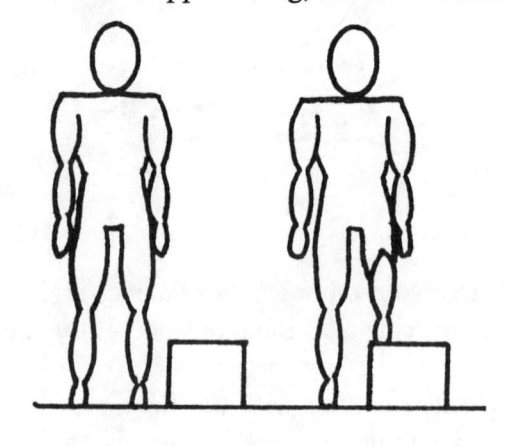

Sports Medicine: The New Field Of Injury Prevention

C. Repeat to fatigue.
D. Turn around, repeat in opposite direction.
Note: Maintain good trunk posture — flat low back, abdomen firm throughout this exercise. This exercise is done with no weights.

SHOULDER, ARM AND WRIST EXERCISES

1. Horizontal Front And Side Lift
Exercise Benefits: Deltoid, Shoulder, Girdle, Upper Chest
Starting Position: Stand with feet comfortably spread, arms at sides holding dumbbells.
Exercise Action:
  A. Slowly forward lift dumbbells in front of you and hold for two seconds.

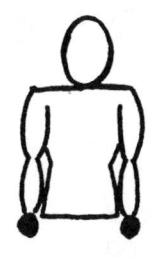

  B. Slowly move arms out to side position while maintaining the horizontal position and hold for two seconds. Then slowly lower to sides.

2. Tricep Stretch-Press
Exercise Benefits: Shoulder stretch, Tricep strength
Starting Position: Stand with feet comfortably balanced, holding a dumbbell weight in each hand fully overhead. Keep low back flat, abdomen firm, chin in.
Exercise Action:
  A. Slowly lower dumbbells behind head to full elbow bend and feel front shoulder stretch.
  B. Slowly raise dumbbells to starting position.
Note: Keep elbow close to ear and pointing up toward the ceiling throughout the exercise.

3. Forearm Flexor And Extensor Curl

Exercise Benefits: Improves forearm (wrist) flexors and extensors.

Starting Position: Sit in a chair, forearm resting on the chair arm or a table, with the hand extending beyond the edge. Palm of hand up for flexor, down for extensor exercise.

Exercise Action:

A. Flexor: Lift (flex) wrist to the maximum, hold for 5 seconds and slowly lower. Progress to 5-pound weight maximum.

B. Extensor: Lift (extend) wrist to maximum, hold for 5 seconds, release. Progress to 3-pound weight maximum.

4. Forearm Rotation

Exercise Benefits: Improves forearm rotator muscles. Strengthens wrist.

Starting Position: Sit in a chair, forearm resting on the chair arm or a table, with the hand extending beyond the edge.

Exercise Action: Rotate hand from palm-down to palm-up to palm-down position continuously to fatigue. Progress to 5-pound weight maximum.

5. Isometric Forearm Extensor Exercise (No Weight)

Improves strength of forearm extensors. Hold arm extended close to horizontal in front of body. Actively pull fingers and wrist into fully extended position and hold for five seconds. Progress to 10 repetitions.

6. Isometric Forearm Extensor And Flexor Exercises (No Weight)

Improves strength of forearm flexors and extensors. Hold arm as in exercise #5. Squeeze tennis ball and hold for five seconds. Progress to 10 repetitions.

7. Extensor Flexibility (No Weight)

Improves flexibility of forearm extensors used primarily in heavy muscled persons. Hold arm as in Exercise #5. Stretch wrist toward floor using opposite hand. Hold for five seconds and release. Progress to five repetitions. Strive for 80 degrees of wrist flexion from horizontal.

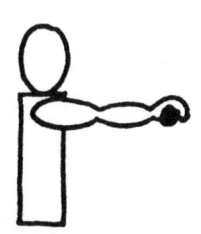

LOWER BACK AND ABDOMINAL EXERCISES

Proper form has been emphasized as an important procedure for all exercises, but it becomes even more important in performing back exercises. Never jerk the back motion or arch your back during the exercise action, since this could cause strain or injury.

Remember, strengthening your abdominal supporting muscles is the primary objective. Certain exercises start by pushing the back flat against the floor. When your abdominal muscles push the lower back against the floor, this motion simultaneously tends to tilt your pelvis upward. This often is referred to as pelvic tilt. Practice this coordinated action. It not only helps strengthen your abdominal muscles, but also reduces back stress when you are standing or sitting. (Note: no weights for these exercises)

1. Single Knee To Chest Stretch

Keeping the lower back pushed flat, pull your right knee toward your chest and hold it there with your hands. Pull your knee far enough to feel a stretch in the buttocks. Hold for

5 seconds. Repeat with the other leg. Do each leg 10 times.
Progression:
    A. Tuck in your chin, raise your head and shoulders off the floor and bring your forehead as close to your knee as you can.
    B. Finally progress to having your forehead touch the knee.
    C. Repeat 10 times each.

2. Pectoral Stretch

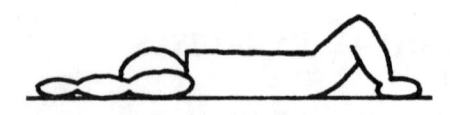

With the knees bent and the feet flat, tilt the pelvis to flatten the lower back. Hold the back flat and extend both arms overhead. Try to touch the entire arm (shoulders, elbows and wrists) to the floor with elbows straight. Bring upper arms as close to the sides of the head as possible. Hold for 5 seconds. Repeat 3 times. Note: Your lower back must be held flat throughout the exercise.

3. Curl-Ups

Lie on back, knees bent, hands across chest. Start with pelvic tilt — tighten your abdominal muscles, lift your buttocks slightly off the floor and flatten your back against the floor. Tuck your chin toward your chest and slowly lift your head and shoulders off the floor. Hold this position for 3 seconds. Slowly lower. Do 5 to 10 repetitions.

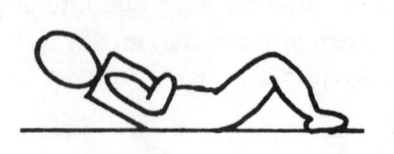

Progression: Lie on back, knees bent and pointing away

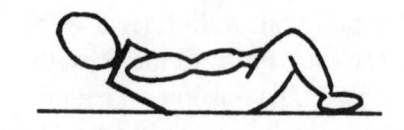

Sports Medicine: The New Field Of Injury Prevention

from each other, soles of feet pressed together and arms outstretched. Slowly curl up as far as you can. Hold for 3 seconds. Slowly lower. Do 5 to 10 repetitions.

4. Side Twist Sit-Ups

Start with the pelvic tilt. Rotate your shoulders to the right (your left shoulder will come off the floor). Tuck in your chin and slowly lift your right shoulder until it is off the floor. Hold this position for 3 seconds. Your arms should be outstretched along your right side. Slowly lower. Do 5 to 10 repetitions. Repeat to the left side.

Progression: Repeat the same process, but with the hands across your chest. Do 5 to 10 repetitions.

5. Elevated Leg Crunches

Lie on your back on the floor with calves resting on a chair. Slowly curl head, shoulders and arms forward as far as possible. Hold for 3 seconds, then slowly lower. Do 5-10 repetitions.

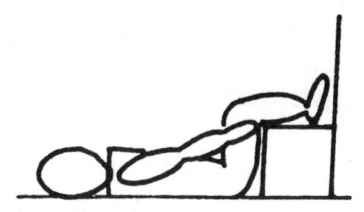

6. Hip Raise

Exercise Benefits: Abdomen, Buttocks

Starting Position: Lie on back, exercise knee bent with foot flat on floor. Opposite leg should be held straight and lifted 18" off floor throughout the exercise. Arms at side for balance. Do not arch low back.

Exercise Action:

A. Tighten buttocks and abdominal muscles while lifting hips off floor to maximum height. Hold for 5 seconds.

B. Return to starting position and exercise other leg.

C. Repeat to fatigue.

7. Arm-Leg Lift
   Exercise Benefits: Upper and Lower Back muscles.

Starting Position: Lie with pillow under your stomach.
Exercise Action:
   A. Raise right arm and left leg up from the floor about 6". Hold for three seconds and return to starting position.
   B. Repeat with left arm and right leg. Do 5 to 10 repetitions.

CALF, ANKLE AND FOOT EXERCISES

Do all exercises slowly and smoothly. Start with five repetitions and progress to 20 repetitions gradually. For exercises No. 4 and No. 5, start with a two-pound weight and progress to a five-pound weight. Maintain balance by holding a stair rail in exercise No. 1, and touching the wall in exercise No. 2. (No weights)

1. Step Calf Stretch And Raise
   Exercise Benefits: Calf Muscles.
   Starting Position: Stand on edge of step, balancing on balls of feet with one hand on railing or against a wall.
   Exercise Action:
      A. Slowly lower body so heels are well below edge of step,

Sports Medicine: The New Field Of Injury Prevention

fully stretching heel cord. Do not bounce. Hold for 3 seconds.

    B. Slowly raise up on tip-toes. Hold for 3 seconds. Return to starting position.

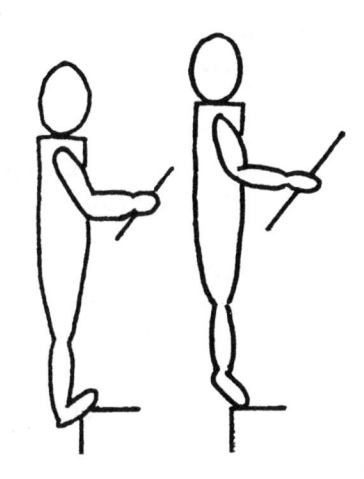

2. Heel Swing
Exercise Benefits: Outside muscles of outer leg and ankle.
Starting Position: Stand with feet parallel, 4" apart.
Exercise Action:
    A. Slowly raise up on toes, swing heels outward.
    B. Swing heels inward.
    C. Return to starting position and repeat
Note: Wear shoes or socks for this exercise.

3. Toe Curl
Exercise Benefits: Muscles along arch of foot.
Starting Position: Sit with bare feet on floor on the edge of towel. Place a one to two-pound weight on far end of towel.
Exercise Action: Curl toes over towel, repeatedly pulling towel and weight toward you. Repeat 3-5 times.

4. Foot Extensor Curl

Exercise Benefits: Foot and leg extensors.

Starting Position: Sit comfortably on edge of bench or chair, legs dangling, with knees at 90-degree angle. Hold edge firmly.

Exercise Action:

　　A. Slowly raise (dorsi-flex) your foot to highest level.

　　B. Lower to starting position (two seconds to raise; two to lower).

　　C. Repeat with opposite foot.

5. Foot Eversion (Toe Out)

Exercise Benefits: Foot and leg everters (Ankle Outer Muscles)

Starting position: Lie on a bed or table on your side. Keep your pelvis straight. The exercise leg is on top and the foot and ankle should hang over the end of the bed or table. Position the weight on the foot. For balance, bend the other leg at knee underneath exercise leg.

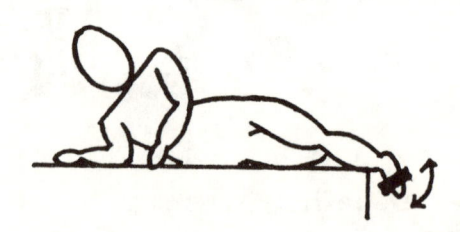

Exercise Action:

　　A. Slowly toe the foot out, raising the weight to the maximum level you can reach.

Sports Medicine: The New Field Of Injury Prevention

B. Return to starting position for repetitions.
C. Repeat exercise with opposite ankle and foot (two seconds to raise, two seconds to lower).

FLEXIBILITY EXERCISES

The three exercises described here should be done in conjunction with the four stretching exercises noted in Chapter III, Getting Started. They should only be done after you have warmed up and are most effective at the end of an exercise session.

In each exercise, stretch as far as you can, going just short of discomfort. Hold for 6 seconds. Then inhale deeply and as you exhale, stretch a bit more, still without causing any pain. Hold this fully stretched position for 10 to 15 seconds, breathing easily. Repeat each exercise 3 times.

1. Trunk Side Bend
   Exercise Benefits: Iliotibial Band (Outer Hip and Thigh Muscles)
   Starting Position: Stand with both legs straight, exercise leg crossed as far behind the non-exercise leg as possible.
   Exercise Action: Side bend as far as you can toward non-exercise side, sliding non-exercise arm down non-exercise leg. Do not rotate trunk. Goal is to have trunk at a 45-degree angle.

2. Adductor (Groin) Stretch
   ExerciseBenefits: Groin Muscles
   Starting Position: Stand with legs as far apart as possible. Keep abdominal muscles firm.
   Exercise Action:
   A. Place exercise hand on exercise knee and

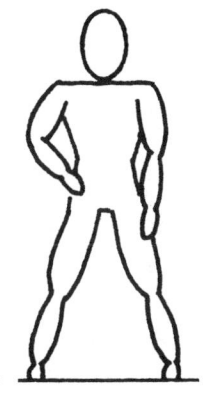

opposite hand on opposite hip.

B. Slowly bend exercise knee until thigh is parallel to floor, stretching the groin area in the process. Roll onto inner side of foot while keeping foot on floor during stretch.

Caution: Do not cause pain.

3. Wall Stretch

Exercise Benefits: Gastrocnemius, Soleus (Calf and Achilles Tendon).

Starting Position: Stand facing the wall, exercise leg behind other leg. Place hands against wall for balance. Keep body in straight line throughout exercise and do not let back foot rotate out.

Exercise Action:

A. Holding exercise knee straight and keeping heel flat, bend other knee while leaning trunk forward. Do not arch your low back. Feel stretch in calf.

B. Slightly blend exercise knee and raise heel about 1" off the floor, then lean forward toward the wall. Feel stretch near heel.

Note: Toes and foot of exercise leg must be pointing forward throughout the exercise.

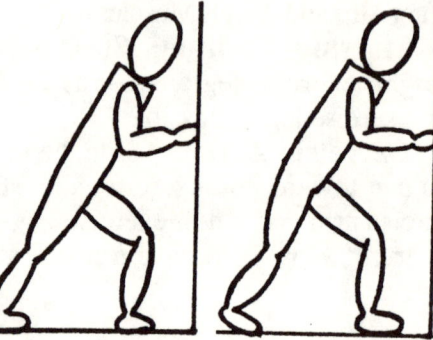

CAUTIONARY NOTES

1. The exercises described here should be only initiated after you are comfortably doing the exercise programs detailed in Chapter III, Getting Started.

2. If you have had a previous injury affecting a joint in any of the body areas to be strengthened, do not

commence these exercises without first checking with your doctor.

3. If you have pain of any kind while executing a particular exercise, stop immediately. The next time you exercise, try fewer repetitions and less weight or no weight at all. If pain persists, check with your doctor.

4. Do not exercise a joint area if swelling or inflammation exists there (feeling heat around an area is an indication of inflammation). If swelling and/or inflammation remain more than 72 hours, check with your doctor. Treat the swelling with ice, not heat.

5. Any injury that causes significant discomfort — where the pain does not moderate in 24 hours — warrants checking with your doctor. As you learn about your body's weaker and stronger areas, you can adjust your conditioning efforts accordingly. It is important to not let a weak area develop into a chronic condition in which continuing discomfort leads to greater weakness.

HEALTH SPAS, FITNESS CENTER AND HOME GYMNASIUMS

The exercises reviewed in this chapter are not the only way to strengthen specific areas of the body. Today, many urban and suburban communities offer various types of health and fitness centers or clubs, which generally provide a fairly wide range of body strengthening equipment. In turn, manufacturers of such equipment also have designed special, multi-purpose home fitness equipment to serve those who prefer this convenience, or to exercise in privacy.

For the most part, such equipment is reliable, although it is expensive to purchase. When used properly and under knowledgeable instruction, it is effective for strength building. The danger, both from the usual weight machine equipment at fitness centers as well as the multi-purpose home gyms, is that they very easily can subject you to load forces that are injurious and not beneficial. Most of these machines are designed to accommodate the force loads needed to build muscle strength in the average young body. If you have maintained good condition over the years and have worked extensively with this type of exercise equipment, a home gym may fit some of your specialized needs. While membership in a professionally staffed fitness center is not inexpensive, it can provide the guidance and supervision for proper use of this equipment. The good ones will also insist that you have a complete medical exam before commencing a program at their facility.

An alternative and complementary method for maintaining a strengthening program at home can be accomplished through a simple, but effective, device called the Iso-Flex, a type of resistance tube.

This device (photos pp. 207 & 208) easily controls resistance using a flexible tension exercise cord. Since the exercise intensity is totally controlled by the user, overload is minimized. The Velcro vertical and horizontal attachment allows the Iso-Flex to be used for lower body as well as for upper body exercise. Developed by the Virginia Sportsmedicine Institute in coordination with the Research Division of Medical Sports, Inc., the Iso-Flex system is safe and easy to use with its detailed instructional manual and can be obtained through Medical Sports, Inc., P.O. Box 7187, Arlington, Virginia 22207.

As the photos illustrate, the Iso-Flex can be adapted to a wide range of upper and lower body strengthening exercises. It has the extra advantages of needing no storage space, fits conveniently into a briefcase for travel, and requires no preparation for use, although regular warm up before use applies here too.

From the standpoint of aerobic conditioning, there are two other pieces of home fitness equipment that can be extremely useful.

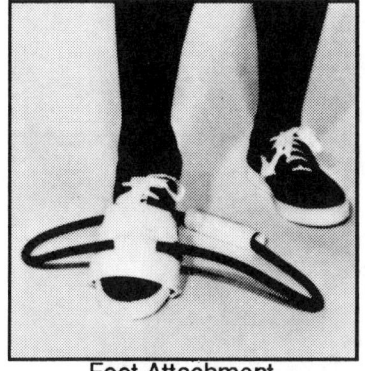

Sports Medicine: The New Field Of Injury Prevention

Foot Attachment

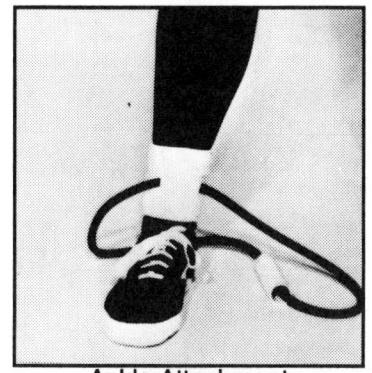

Ankle Attachment

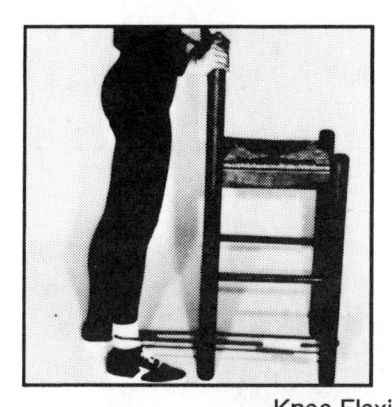

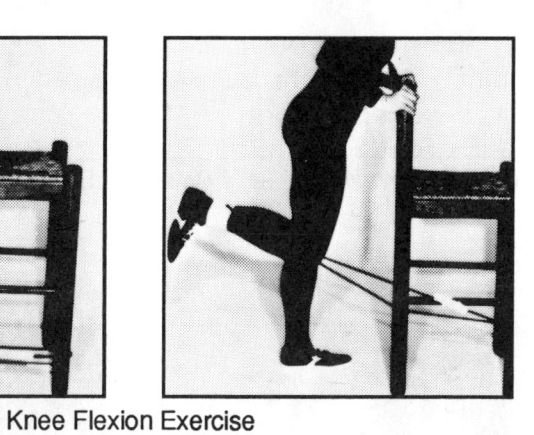

Knee Flexion Exercise
Starting Position — Exercise Action

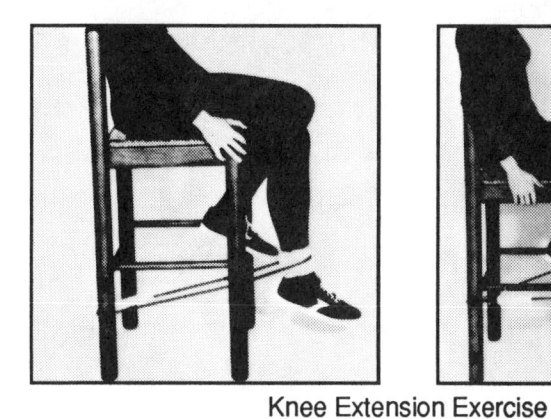

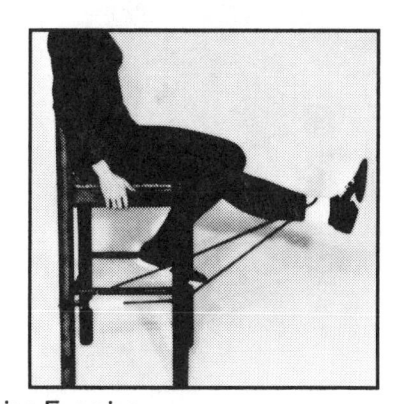

Knee Extension Exercise
Starting Position — Exercise Action

SPORTS AFTER 50

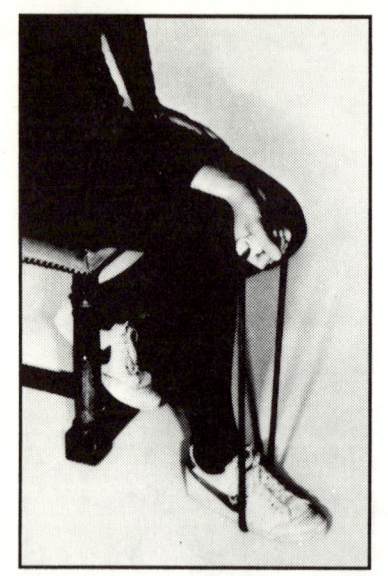

Flexor Wrist Curl Exercise
Starting Position — Exercise Action

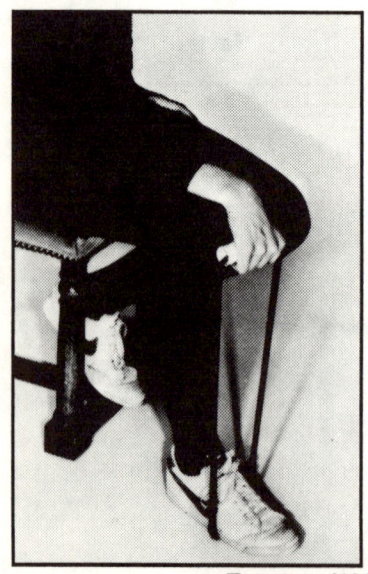

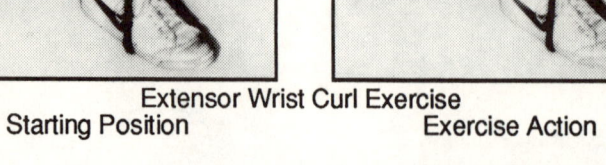

Extensor Wrist Curl Exercise
Starting Position — Exercise Action

Sports Medicine: The New Field Of Injury Prevention

One is the stationary bicycle. It is a useful device, not only in the Getting Started program, but also for maintaining aerobic fitness. These stationary bicycles come with several kinds of measuring devices and a wide resistance range than can be easily controlled. Some work the arms as well as the legs.

The most important features are strong construction with a rigid frame, a solid platform for balance and a heavy, well balanced flywheel that allows a smooth pedaling motion at all resistance levels.

A second item worth considering is the small trampoline. It has several advantages:

- It allows the pleasure of jogging, yet the trampoline minimizes shock to the ankles, knees and hips.
- It can be used indoors as well as outside.
- It is reasonably inexpensive ($100 or less) and can be easily rolled into a closet for storage, and
- With a bar (as pictured), the beginner can balance safely while running in place, taking care to stay in the middle of the trampoline and to avoid hitting the metal frame around the perimeter.

For the person who has completed the Getting Started program, the trampoline and the indoor stationary bicycle provide alternative aerobic training choices for bad weather. They are simple and safe to use, are affordable for most and will enable you to maintain and/or advance your fitness.

CHAPTER VIII
Go For It?

What, if anything, is important about risk-taking? In fact, what exactly is healthy, as opposed to unhealthy, risk, and why should those of us 50-and-over be interested in or concerned about this subject? Aren't all risky situations to be avoided as one ages? "Go for it!" may be the exuberant cry of the spectator, but spectators don't have to pay the price of failure. The more typical attitude is, "At my age, who needs additional risk?"

Such recognizable concerns — not surprising in an era in which the dangers from nuclear explosion or from other environment-destroying forces appear to be multiplying — have led many to perceive risk-taking only in purely negative terms, i.e., risk-taking is dangerous, so try to avoid it.

Yet, evidence indicates that eliminating risk opportunities as we age can lead subtly but steadily to a withdrawal from active life. Situations that demand difficult decisions, present complicated choices, or simply offer new options, increasingly will tend to be avoided. In turn, one's interests and perceptions inevitably will narrow, thus accelerating this constricting cycle of withdrawal.

It is quite clear, however, that the above is not a necessary pattern of aging. We all know individuals in their eighties or older who continue to embark on new ventures, enthusiastically enroll in continuing education programs, or plunge into avocations they never had time for when younger. Regular physical activity and, where possible, sport participation seem to remain a part of their lives, too. In sum, challenge and personal commitment of various kinds provide constant stimulation for them.

Medical experts admit they don't know the underlying reasons why some individuals seem to become old as early as their late forties, while others are productive and creative into their nineties. As this book has argued, physical fitness can be a major factor in the quality of life as one ages. There are some, though, whose energy level and productive capabilities remain high despite serious illness and/or other physical handicaps. What sets these individuals apart is sheer willpower, the determination to utilize their limited physical resources to the maximum. Fortunately, the ingredients comprising productive physical fitness are now well recognized and the importance of appropriate fitness for all age levels is no longer debated.

The experts are much less sure about the other factors affecting good mental and emotional health as we age. As the search for answers goes on, it seems significant that the subject of risk-taking is receiving renewed attention. Certainly, in a society so conditioned to worrying about the bad effects of stress and so anxious to reduce emotional strain (witness the rise in annual sales of Valium and other stress-relieving pills) it is hardly astonishing that some important values in the risk-taking process often have been overlooked.

Part of the problem is that intelligent or healthy risks are not always easy to distinguish from unwarranted ones. The simplistic view that all risk is dangerous then becomes too readily accepted. The resulting tendency is to think of risk only in the extreme; that is, situations that invite serious physical risk, major economic damage or severe emotional hurt.

Genuine risk does demand confronting fear. It cannot be something synthetic or a game. A healthy risk, however, should not entail dangers that are too severe. Put another way, the possibility of failure has to be faced, but its consequences should not be overwhelming. From a different, but equally valid perspective, to have never failed is to have never risked. To accept challenge always means accepting some risk.

Gor For It?

Healthy risk stimulates and energizes. But, because each person is different in emotional makeup and in other personal attributes, there are no absolutes in comparing types of risks. Physical risks, for instance, are relatively easy for some individuals to accept. These are usually viewed as the daredevil type of personality. On the other hand, that same kind of person may avoid situations in which he or she might have to entertain an audience or lead a public discussion. Conversely, the person who shies away from physical risk may enjoy "on stage" appearances and sees little risk in the possibility of public embarrassment or failure.

As Ralph Keyes concludes in his thought-provoking and very readable book, *Chancing It*: "Taking risks willy-nilly is not what we need to do. Nor is advising others to take more chances. Depending upon who we are, when, and where, creating a balanced diet of genuine risk can mean taking more of some kinds of risks, fewer of others. And avoiding like the plague risks urged on us by others, which may be theirs but not ours.

"To stay alive and lively, we need a steady diet of risk. But we're the only ones who can assess what that means. The assessment of others isn't what matters, nor the size of the risk, or its potential to thrill. All that matters is that a risk be genuine. And no one knows but the risk-taker the meaning of genuine risk."

The point that Keyes makes so eloquently is that healthy risk must be determined on an individual basis. At the same time, criteria for such risks will constantly change for each of us. We benefit from failure as well as success in healthy risk-taking. Knowing failure is not fatal, we subsequently can more freely accept other kinds of risks that might be healthy for us. Perhaps the special value lies in the constant interplay of challenge, acceptance of risk, stimulation through accomplishment, yet recognition that failure, too, has benefits.

Nor should you be amazed to discover that sports can fit nicely into this picture. Challenge can be found at any level, from the first day onward to whatever skill level you may reach. If you are a person whose life patterns already contain a variety of healthy challenges, the risk elements in sport participation may be superfluous and the enjoyable physical exercise alone will be value enough. But for many of us 50-and-older, sports also can present benefits beyond just fitness considerations.

As in other endeavors, of course, you can set impossible achievement goals in sports and remain always frustrated. Or you can establish realistic objectives that can be accomplished. You will fail, occasionally. You may even look foolish once in a while, but the pleasure of reaching a new skill level will always stimulate you.

The desire to improve one's performance contains risk, and the willingness to actually attempt this step opens the door to failure. The patience to practice and the motivation to try again, however, are always your options. They also remain a foolproof formula for achieving a level of success which will further encourage you.

And should you venture into seniors competition, you will find others like yourself being challenged, occasionally frustrated, but learning and enjoying. No question, such competition presents different kinds of risk. There is not only an audience to witness your mistakes, but you will sometimes feel that special disappointment of knowing you performed below your capabilities. Don't worry; that's normal. Everyone goes through that experience. Your fellow competitors will encourage you, not ridicule you. "Welcome to the group. We all have those days", is what you will hear.

What about sharing your new skills and knowledge with others? Helping someone else to learn and enjoy your sport can be a totally new challenge. It will force you to think about the sport in new ways, to articulate effectively its key concepts, demonstrate its techniques and find successful ways to communicate all this to beginners.

Oh sure, the risk of failure is here, too. But try it. Instructing will even improve your own skills!

The real point is to use your sports to the fullest. You can't really go wrong. You will have fun; you will become more fit; and you will be more ready to involve yourself in other activities.

Should you risk it? The answer seems clear. This is the very time in your life to "Go for it!"

Illustration Credits

Photographs

Cover: Windsurfing Hilton Head, Eric Horan, Uniphoto, Mark Jenkinson

Chapter II:

Boardsailing: p. 37, Windsurfing Hilton Head
remaining photos, author

Bicycling: p. 48, Cynthia Chess
p. 50, "Over The Hill Gang", Denver, Colorado
remaining photos, author

Rowing: p. 51 Mark Jenkinson
p. 52 Donald Carmichael
remaining photos, author

Racquet Sports: Author

Canoeing: p. 94, author
remaining photos, Glen Mowbray

Skiing: p. 99, 100, 101 and 110, author
p. 103, 105, 107, 108 and 109, "Over The Hill Gang"
p. 106, 112 and 113, Dean Mendell, Nordic Adventures, Rochester, Vermont

Swimming: Author

Small Boat Sailing: p. 122 Eric Skemp
remaining photos, author

Chapter VII   p. 207 and 208, Medical Sports, Inc.
p. 209, Cynthia Chess

215

SPORTS AFTER 50

Illustration Credits Continued

Medical Drawings

Chapter III   p. 140 and 141, Lynn Mills,
                     Virginia Sportsmedicine Institute
                     p. 149 through 156, Maja Welch,
                     Virginia Sportsmedicine Institute

Chapter VII   p. 186, 187 and 188, Diagrams courtesy of
                     Living Anatomy, Faber 1948, R.D. Lockhart,
                     Professor Emeritus, Aberdeen University,
                     Scotland
                     p. 192 through 204, Maja Welch